PROWLER

U.S. Half-tracks

The development and deployment of the U.S. Army's half-track based multiple gun motor carriages and gun motor carriages

Written by
David Doyle
Edited by Pat Stansell

Dedicated to the crewmen of U.S. half-tracks of all nationalities. Without your experiences and sacrifices, there would be no books such as this.

Published by The Ampersand Group, Inc.,
A HobbyLink Japan Company
235 NE 6th Ave., Suite B, Delray Beach FL 33483-5543
www.ampersandpubco.com
ISBN: 978-0-9861127-4-4

Front cover: The M3 75mm Gun Motor Carriage was used extensively by the US Army in the early part of WWII, and by the US Marines throughout the conflict. This Marine Corps example is owned and restored by Brent Mullins. (Author)

Rear cover top: The M16 Multiple Gun Motor Carriage, armed with four .50-caliber machine guns, was the longest serving example of US half-track, remaining in the American arsenal well beyond the end of the Korean war. This example is owned and restored by Paul Viens. (Author)

Rear cover, bottom: The M15A1 Combination Gun Motor Carriage was fielded alongside the M16, but was armed by a pair of .50 caliber machine guns and a 37mm auto cannon. This example was restored by Mike Keller. (Rick Forys)

Title page: Among the heavily armed variants of the American half-track was the 75mm Howitzer Motor Carriage T30. The cutouts in the lower left corners of the shields to accommodate the drivers are apparent in this wartime view. On the closest vehicle, marked in white on the inside of the folding flap of the driver's door and also on the side of the vehicle to the rear of that door is "75MM." On the hood of the nearest T30, the registration number is faintly visible: 4042505. (Jim Gilmore collection)

Front end paper: The nickname "PROWLER" is painted on the driver's door of this 81mm Mortar Carrier M4A1 photographed for the Armored Board at Fort Knox, Kentucky. No U.S. Army registration number is visible. A .30-caliber machine gun is on the front of the skate rail, and to the rear of the gun is a radio antenna. (Kevin Emdee collection)

Rear end paper: Using a new Army method of loading a half-track on a railroad car, a Half-Track Combination Gun Motor Carriage M15A1 and a hitched trailer are secured to a flatcar at Kaftertal, West Germany, on 24 November 1953. The half-track has markings for the 62nd Antiaircraft Artillery Battalion, Seventh U.S. Army. (NARA)

Table of contents: U.S. half-tracks with weapons mounts played a critical role in providing the Army and Marines with fire-support and anti-aircraft defense during World War II and the Korean War. Prominent in both of those roles was the Half-Track Multiple Gun Motor Carriage M16, armed with a quadruple .50-caliber machine gun turret, an example of which is leading a Jeep and a CCKW truck along a street in Europe toward the end of World War II. (NARA)

Image Credits: American Truck Historical Society (ATHS); Clark County Historical Society; Jim Gilmore; Wayne Hlavin collection; Imperial War Museum (IWM); Library of Congress, Office of War Information collection (LOC); Jim Mesko; National Archives and Records Administration (NARA); Office of History, US Army Corps of Engineers; Patton Museum of Cavalry and Armor (Patton Museum); Rock Island Arsenal Museum; TACOM LCMC History Office; Third Cavalry Museum; US Army Air Defense Artillery Museum; US Army Chemical Corps Museum; US Army Ordnance Museum; (Ordnance Museum); US Army Quartermaster Museum (Quartermaster);US Army Transportation Museum; USMC; Tom Wolboldt; Wisconsin Historical Society and Steve Zaloga.

Book design by Patrick Stansell.

Table of Contents

Preface

Whether it be from Hollywood, toys from our youth, carefully fashioned scale models or wartime photographs, it seems that for many one of the first images brought to mind when the words "U.S. half-track" are uttered is that of a vehicle bristling with four heavy machine guns. That vehicle, the M16, is a Multiple Gun Motor Carriage, and it along with its ilk as well as mortar carriers, and gun and howitzer motor carriages, are the subject of this volume. These vehicles were all based on the half-track cars and personnel carriers covered so extensively in Part 1 of this book.

While not ideal in terms of off-road performance and armor protection, U.S. produced half-tracks were mechanically reliable, easily maintained, simple to produce, and thanks to the American automotive industry, were produced in massive quantities. These attributes led to half-tracks being used for the basis of the myriad of vehicles described in this volume.

These vehicles fell into the same two large groups as those described in Part 1: Standard Nomenclature List (SNL) G-102 vehicles, produced by White, Autocar and Diamond T primarily for use by U.S. forces, and the SNL G-147 vehicles, produced by International Harvester principally for Defense Aid requirements.

Early on many in the U.S. Army preferred fully tracked vehicles to half-tracks, in many reasons for good cause. Fully tracked vehicles offered improved off-road mobility and the potential for parts commonality with the tanks that these vehicles were expected to operate in conjunction with. However, fully tracked vehicles were more expensive to purchase and operate, and often had longer development and manufacturing lead times. There was also a critical shortage of manufacturing capacity for tanks, especially during the early part of WWII. U.S. tank production early in WWII relied upon locomotive and rail car manufacturers, accustomed to building large, heavy vehicles, before shifting to purpose-built, government-owned, contractor-operated plants.

On the other hand, it was truck manufacturers in existing plants that built half-tracks. Unlike a tank, which is comprised almost solely of components

Above: *U.S. Army half-tracks had just begun what would become over a decade of service when this pair of T12 Gun Motor Carriages were photographed crossing a country road near Lancaster, NC. while on maneuvers in late November 1941. (PAS)*

Opposite: *A rare 40mm Gun Motor Carriage M34 of Battery C, 40th Antiaircraft Artillery Battalion, is situated in a well-prepared dugout lined with steel drums and sandbags, at Yokohama, Japan, on 7 August 1951. The registration number is faintly visible on the hood: 4062013. (NARA)*

engineered and constructed to be a tank component, U.S. half-tracks are principally a light-medium truck sheathed in armor, with a purpose-engineered rear suspension. This led to both the advantage in cost and manufacturing and to the less than ideal military characteristics.

As with the vehicles of Part I, much has been written about the vehicles in this book since the last one rolled off an assembly line over 70 years ago. Most of the prior books on the subject are now out of print, some are outright erroneous, and as a result, the complete picture is not presented.

Richard Hunnicutt's *Half-track, A History of American Semi-Tracked Vehicles* provides an excellent overview of the development process from the Army point of view. Using that work as a benchmark, with this volume we have endeavored to expand the coverage to incorporate material from the manufacturer's perspective as well as illuminating the field and combat use of the vehicles. Information of benefit to those involved in vehicle preservation and restoration, including registration numbers, contract numbers, delivery dates and modification work orders, has been located and incorporated.

Collecting the material for these books consumed well over a decade, and was an ongoing process. Not surprisingly, after Part I was published additional information came to light that ideally would have been included in that volume. This material is presented in a series of addendums at the back of this volume.

This book is structured a bit differently than Part I. In this book, we move through the development and production of all the vehicles, grouped by type, before plunging into a chronological presentation of in-service photographs without regard to vehicle configuration.

Also omitted from this volume are line drawings. With the wealth of original photos from many perspectives, the inclusion of line drawings was judged to be not warranted. Additionally, when one analyses the existing line drawings, the many complex shapes and assemblies of the various weapons become lost in simple, four-view drawings. The intensive photographic coverage will answer many more questions.

While many of the photographs in this book have only appeared in obscure works, and some have not been previously published at all, it is inevitable that when attempting to completely cover a subject such as this, some of the photos will have been published previously. While long-time enthusiasts may

have books on the shelf containing some of these images, to do so requires many books, none of which are currently in print. This scarcity presents a problem for the enthusiast just becoming interested, and awkward to manage even for the "old-timer" who must thumb through several volumes seeking a tidbit of information contained in a photo.

By collecting these into this two-volume set, augmenting them with many new images, and through modern production techniques and high production standards, we allow the reader to see these with new quality in a single place.

Acknowledgments

It is not possible for a single person, or even a pair of authors, to write a book of this scope. Rather, what you hold now in your hands is the result of an extensive and broad collaboration. Were the input of any one of the friends and colleagues listed below be removed, then this

book would be measurably different.

Joe DeMarco, who has spent countless hours researching U.S. Army Ordnance during WWII, provided thoughtful insights into the production, registration and Ordnance serial numbers of the half-tracks.

Jim Gilmore, who has a vast collection of archival documents and photos, not only opened his collection for this project, but also took time out of his own research at the National Archives to dig up additional elusive documents for this project.

Tom Kailbourn's careful and detailed analysis of many of the photos in this volume was invaluable, and he contributed immeasurably to the information presented herein.

Kevin Lockwood, prominent half-track historian, collector and preservationist, reviewed and corrected the manuscript, and provided thoughtful insights into the various field modifications performed by certain army units.

Kip Lindberg, Director of the U.S. Army

Chemical Corps Museums, provided fresh material concerning efforts to mount 4.2-inch mortars in half-tracks and scout cars.

Jonathon Bernstein, author and director of the U.S. Army Air Defense Artillery Museum, not only provide vintage photos, but also lent his expertise to sorting out details of the field use of the vehicles.

Scott Taylor lent a critical eye to the manuscript, providing corrections and amplification from the combined standpoints of writer, historian and modeler.

Fellow author, vehicle collector and historian Pat Ware supplied elusive documentation on the Commonwealth use of half-tracks, covering both the WWII and post-war eras.

Veteran authors and researchers Steve Zaloga and Jim Mesko gladly provided photographs from their extensive collections.

Tom Wolboldt has spent countless hours analyzing U.S. military vehicle production during WWII and has developed extensive databases as a result of this research. Tom willingly shared this information, as well as items from his document and photo collection, to further this volume.

Lee Young, librarian and archivist for the American Truck Historical Society, graciously opened the Society's extensive White holdings for review, including numerous previously unpublished photos.

The former staff of the Patton Museum, Frank Jardim, Charles Lemons and Candace Fuller, allowed unfettered access to their extensive holdings, including the extensive collections donated by Col. Robert Icks and historian R. P. Hunnicutt. When a personal visit was not possible, Don Moriarty graciously copied whatever materials were needed.

The staffs of the Military History Institute, Benson Ford Archives, Historical Society of Pennsylvania, Library of Congress, U.S. Army Ordnance Museum, TACOM LCMC History Office, PT Boats, Incorporated and the U.S. National Archives were without exception enthusiastic supporters of this effort, allowing access, providing suggestions and quickly responding to many queries.

However, the most enthusiastic and unflagging support provided for this project came from my darling wife Denise. Denise traveled coast-to-coast, endured hot, dusty archives, and willingly scanned thousands of documents and hundreds of photos during the six-year process that resulted in this volume. Without her support in this project, it would not have been possible.

−David Doyle
Memphis, Fall 2015

Chapter 1: Mortar Carriers

The First Half-Track Mounted Weapons

While the baseline vehicles for standardized U.S. half-tracks during WWII were the M2 half-track car and M3 personnel carrier, discussed in depth in Part One of this series, it was foregone that other variants would be part of the SNL G-102 family, as well. When the Ordnance Committee standardized the two vehicles above on 19 September 1940, per OCM 16112, the Committee also standardized the 81-mm Mortar Carrier, M4, creating the first of many variants.

It was specified that the M4 use the chassis of the M2, and externally the most telling difference between the types is the presence of a rear door on the M4. This door is partially obscured by the machine gun skate rail, which was also carried over from the M2.

The original concept was that the 81mm mortar would be dismounted and fired conventionally from the ground, with the weapon being fired from the vehicle only rarely, and then in extreme circumstances and over the rear of the vehicle. Accordingly, much of the interior space of the vehicle was filled with ammunition racks, with stowage being provided in the pilot vehicle for 112 rounds.

This pilot, although as noted approved in September 1940, was not delivered by White until August 1941, almost a year later. Testing of the vehicle at Aberdeen revealed the need for some improvements.

Among the changes resulting from the Aberdeen testing was reduction of the ammunition stowage, down to 96 rounds, to provide additional space for the mortar crew. With the testing complete, production of the M4 began by White, the sole producer of the type.

The M4 was to be armed with the 81mm mortar M1 with both vehicle and ground mounts; a .30-caliber M1917A1 Browning machine gun; a .50-caliber M2 Browning Machine gun: tripod mounts for each; and a .45-caliber M1928A1 Thompson submachine gun. In addition to the 96 rounds of 81mm ammunition, the vehicle also carried 6,000 rounds of .30-caliber, 750 rounds of .50-caliber, and 550 rounds of .45-caliber ammunition, the latter being furnished as 20-20 round and 3-50 round magazines.

The Summary Report of Tank-Automotive Material Acceptances indicates that there were three contracts, and three production order numbers, issued for these vehicles. The initial contract, issued in October 1940 for 279 vehicles (including the pilot), was W-741-ORD-6285, production order T-540. But for the pilot, all of these vehicles were delivered in March of 1942.

Also delivered in 1942 were 93 vehicles produced on contract W-303-ORD-1179, production order T-3186, and 200 vehicles procured via contract W-303-ORD-1294, production order T-3374, both issued in February 1942. The latter two contracts were apparently fulfilled concurrently, with 74 of the vehicles being delivered in September 1942 and the remaining 219 being completed in October.

Once in service, it became apparent that for the crews the preferred firing technique was with the mortar mounted in the half-track. Whether this was

The top and bows are removed from this 81mm Mortar Carrier M4A1. The bows and a machine gun tripod are strapped to the tops of the rear storage boxes. Mortar rounds in fiberboard packing tubes are in the bins. The rear door is open, allowing a view of the positioning of the mortar bipod legs on their support. This vehicle has the early-type headlights and brush guards. (Jim Gilmore collection)

because of the exigencies of combat, or merely because of the effort required to remove, emplace and then remount (while navigating past the skate rail) the mortar to fire from ground is not clear.

Nevertheless, the Army recognized this reality, and despite already working on a new model mortar carrier (the M21), set to work improving the traverse of the mortar in order to make firing from the M4 more practical. As delivered, the mortar of the M4 could only be traversed 130 mils using the bipod mount. A traversing fixture was developed that allowed 600-mil traverse in 100 mil increments. The finer traverse capability of the bipod mount was retained. In order to accommodate the wider traversing arc of the mortar, the rear pair of eight-each open-topped ammunition racks was removed, and the socket plate was raised 7 3/8-inches. The 81mm mortar carrier with improved mounting was standardized as the M4A1 on 28 January 1943 per OCM 19607.

Field Service Modification Work order W29 was issued on 18 August 1943 directing the modification of the M4 Mortar Carrier to M4A1 standards. Pursuant to the Standardization recommendation of 28 January, any vehicles that, due to their location, could not be brought up to M4A1 standards would retain their M4 designation, and be reclassified as Limited Standard.

In addition to the conversion of the M4 to M4A1 per the above MWO, White Motor Company was issued two orders for new-build M4A1. Contract W-303-ORD-2078, production order T-4310 for 372 of the vehicles was issued in September 1942, and a further 228 were ordered the next month on W-303-ORD-4011, production order T-4782. Production of these 600 vehicles began with 100 in May 1943, followed by 186 in June, 82 in July, 75 each in August and September, and the last 82 in October 1943.

When production of the next model 81mm Mortar Carrier, the M21, began the M4A1 was reclassified as Limited Standard.

The M21 was the final 81mm Mortar Carrier variant, and unlike the M4 and M4A1, it was based on the longer M3 halftrack, rather than the M2. The M21, designated T19 during development, was the result of the progression of use of the vehicle, as observed by the Armored Force Board. Whereas the M4 was intended as a mortar carrier, with the weapon to be dismounted for firing, the M4A1 was the result of recognizing the advantages of firing from within the vehicle, while the T19 advanced the latter concept by firing forward over the vehicle, negating the need to orient the carrier opposite the direction of advancing forces. The Ordnance Committee approved development of such a vehicle by OCM 18963 on 1 October 1942.

White yet again was turned to for the Mortar Carrier, with a contract being issued in January 1943 for two pilot models. One of the pilots was shipped to the Armored Force Board at Fort Knox, and the other pilot vehicle was delivered to Aberdeen Proving Ground for testing in April 1943. Testing of the new vehicle went smoothly, so smoothly in fact that the Ordnance Committee standardized the T19 as the M21 on 7 June 1943, even before testing was complete. The Standardization was accomplished per OCM 20846.

The Aberdeen testing pointed out only minor deficiencies, only one of which was related to the mortar carrier function itself. That is, the clamp holding the bipod to the sliding rail contacted the center seat at 15-degree right and left traverse, preventing the mortar from being fired in these positions. A minor redesign of the knob on the clamp resolved this.

The other deficiency of note had to do with the pedestal mount for the .50-caliber machine gun. Due to a lack of rigidity, excessive dispersion of the rounds fired was noted, calling for additional stiffener plates to be added.

The armament of the M21 differed slightly from that of its predecessors. In addition to the 81mm mortar, the vehicle was issued with a .50-caliber M2 machine gun and tripod mount, and provisions for a M1903 .30-caliber rifle and a .45-caliber submachine gun. Ammunition stowage consisted of 98 rounds of 81mm ammunition, 300 rounds of .50-caliber, and 554 rounds of .45-caliber

Above: *Developed in the 1930s, the U.S. 81mm Mortar M1 was based on the French Brandt mortar. Featuring a smoothbore tube supported by a bipod and a base plate, the M1 proved to be a highly effective weapon, serving from World War II to the Vietnam War. To increase the mobility of the 81mm Mortar M1, the Army sought a vehicle with a good cross-country capability to transport the weapon, settling on the Half-Track Car M2. (Tom Laemlein)*

Below: *A single Half-Track Car M2 was converted to a production-pilot 81mm Mortar Carrier M4 and was delivered to the U.S. Army in August 1941. This vehicle, which carried U.S. Army registration number (or, U.S.A. number) W-4011785, is viewed from the front while undergoing analysis at Aberdeen Proving Ground, Maryland, on 20 August 1941. This vehicle had an anti-ditching roller. (Patton Museum)*

ammunition, along with 10 HE rifle grenades, 12 MI antitank mines and 12 hand grenades.

Once testing was complete, production was initiated on the Standardized vehicle. Contract W-303-ORD-4011 was amended to include 110 of the new vehicles, which were procured via production order T-10838. Production of the M21 began with 50 vehicles in January 1944, followed by 50 vehicles in February, and concluding with 10 vehicles in March, when all half-track production was halted. At that time there remained an open requirement from Army Service Forces for a further 29 M21s.

4.2-inch Mortar Carriers

While the 81mm infantry mortar saw widespread use, the U.S. Army also fielded a larger mortar, the 4.2-inch (106.6mm) Chemical Mortar. So named because this weapon was fielded by the Chemical Corps, initially for firing smoke, subsequently high explosive rounds were developed for this weapon. Because of the bulk and weight of the 4.2-inch mortar, trials of various motor carriages had begun in the 1920s.

Of particular interest to readers of this volume is the T5E1, a 4.2-inch mortar carrier based on the M3 Scout Car. This vehicle was standardized as the M2, and sources indicate that six examples were produced before the project was halted.

By 16 May 1942 interest in a motor carriage for the 4.2-inch mortar had again risen, and Services of Supply had charged the Ordnance Department with the development of a mechanized mount for the weapon, which was to satisfy the military characteristics set out by the Chemical Corps. These included the capability of firing the weapon from within the vehicle, transport of at least 35 rounds of ammunition as well as the driver, a Chief of Section and a three-man gun squad.

By 20 October 1942 initial firing tests had been conducted at Aberdeen Proving Ground utilizing a M4 81mm Mortar Carrier rearmed with the 4.2-inch Chemical Mortar. In a letter of that date to the Deputy Chief of Ordnance, Lt. Col. Robert J. Icks observed that "...the base plate and cross members of the vehicle frame were not sufficiently strong to

resist the shock impulse of firing." The same letter further "recommends that a Half Track Personnel Carrier M3 with a reinforced frame, as used on the 75 m/m Gun Motor Carriage M3, be forwarded to the Proving Ground. Upon receipt of this vehicle, the 4.2" Mortar will be mounted with a reinforced base plate and a firing test will be performed to determine the suitability of this arrangement as the 4.2" Chemical Mortar Motor Carriage."

Yielding to Icks's recommendation, Lt. Col. Joseph M. Colby's office in Detroit wrote on 5 November 1942 that "...a Half Track Personnel Carrier M3 is being diverted from production and will be shipped from the Autocar Company to your station in the near future for the purpose of mounting the 4.2" Mortar."

Personnel at Aberdeen modified the M3 Personnel Carrier in such a way as to accommodate the 4.2-inch mortar, and by 10 December 1942 firing tests were under way. The initial tests pointed to continuing problems with cross member and bolt strength, requiring further modification. Notable among these was the addition of a Fabreeka (a rubber-impregnated canvas) pad between the spider and the baseplate. Numerous experiments pointed toward the desirability of a 5/8-inch pad in this position. After testing at both Aberdeen and Edgewood Arsenal, the vehicle, by then known as the 4.2-inch Chemical Mortar Carrier T21, was returned to the Autocar plant in order that it could be outfitted for stowage, and installation of secondary armament. Thereafter, the vehicle was returned to Aberdeen for further testing.

Concurrently, the Chemical Warfare Board had revised the desired military characteristics of the vehicle, such that it was thereafter desired that the mortar fire forward over the driver's compartment rather than to the rear. This mimicked the M4A1 to M21 change in the 81-mm mortar carriers.

Development of a vehicle meeting the revised requirements, to be designated the T21E1, was recommended by OCM 21810 on 14 October 1943. The same Ordnance Committee action recommended termination of the rear-firing T21

Above: *As seen on the pilot vehicle, registration number W-4011785, the 81mm Mortar Carrier M4 had an ammunition-bin door to the rear of the driver's door, and a similar ammunition-bin door was on the opposite side of the body. The M4 retained the M2's machine gun skate rail around the inner perimeter of the upper part of the body; part of it is visible above the driver's door. (Patton Museum)*

Below: *Unlike the M2 half-track, the 81mm Mortar Carrier M4 had a door in the rear plate of the body. It was hinged on the right side (facing the exterior), and a latch handle was on the left side. Between the two rear bumperettes was a tow pintle. Above the bumperettes were taillight assemblies, and to the right of the left taillight was an electrical receptacle and cover for trailer light and brake connections. To the left of the door are a bracket and a strap for storing a machine gun tripod. (Patton Museum)*

project. These actions were approved by OCM 21953 shortly thereafter.

Autocar constructed a new pilot, meeting the revised requirements. While this vehicle was purpose-built as a 4.2-inch mortar carrier, it did include all the latest improvements in the G-102 family of vehicles. Further, and arguably key to its design was a 225-pound steel casting to which the mortar baseplate was bolted, and the casting itself was bolted to the vehicle frame.

The T21E1 arrived at Aberdeen on 8 March 1944. Whereas the T21 had been equipped with the then-standard M49 pulpit mount, as was the case with the M21, the forward-firing mortar precluded such an arrangement on the T21E1, as was the case with the M21. Instead, a pedestal mount was provided at the rear of the vehicle for the .50-caliber machine gun.

While test firing of 300 mortar rounds at Aberdeen proved the revised mortar mounting to be adequate, a new problem arose. The overpressure from the firing mortar destroyed the gauges in the instrument panel, in one test even going so far as to strip the vehicle data plate from the dashboard.

To protect against such problems, initially a variety of canvas shields for the instruments were tried, none of which were successful. These were followed by a metal shield, which while effective unfortunately obscured the driver's view of the instruments. The next development was a 1/8-inch steel shield over the entire driver's compartment, which while effective, blocked the line of sight at the minimum elevation of the mortar and center position of the cab. Therefore the shield was modified with a dip at the rear center, relieving this condition.

The T21E1 was transferred to the Chemical Warfare Board at Edgewood Arsenal on 26 April 1944 for service testing. Their tests indicated that some bolts needed to be strengthened and other minor changes made, but that as a whole the vehicle met the requirements.

However, in the interim work had been underway on the T29 4.2-inch mortar carrier, based on the M5A1 light tank chassis, and Headquarters, Army Ground Forces requested that further development efforts on a 4.2-inch mortar carrier be confined to fully-tracked vehicles. As a result, no further work was done on the T21E1 and on 29 March 1945 OCM 27124 terminated work on the half-track based vehicle.

Above: *The rear door of the pilot 81mm Mortar Carrier M4 is open, showing the rearward-pointing 81mm Mortar M1 inside. Originally, it was intended that the mortar crew normally would remove the mortar and emplace it on the ground during combat. The skate rail toward the top of the door opening proved an obstruction that the crew had to contend with when entering or exiting the vehicle. (Kevin Emdee collection)*

Below: *The pilot 81mm Mortar Carrier M4 is viewed from above and to the rear, showing the positioning of the mortar and the early layout of the ammunition bins. To each side of the mortar are bins for eight rounds, next to which are the fuel tanks. Farther forward are two bins with a combined capacity of 40 rounds of 81mm ammo. In front of those two bins are two ammunition compartments with hinged lids, with a combined capacity of 56 81mm rounds. (Patton Museum)*

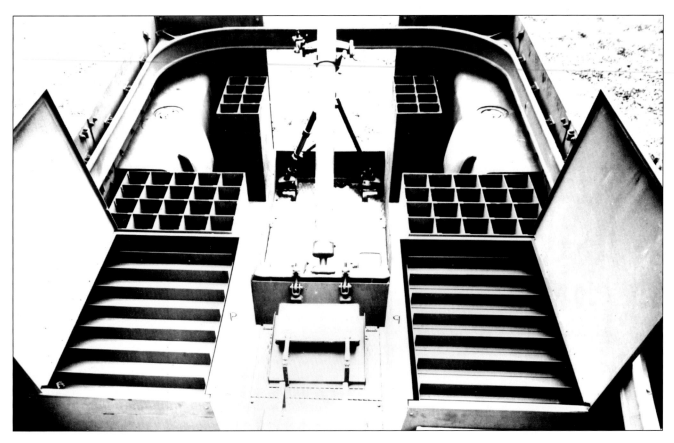

Above: *In another of the series of photos of the pilot M4 taken at Aberdeen Proving Ground on 20 August 1941, the view is from above the cab facing to the rear. In the foreground, the lids of the two ammunition compartments are open, showing the dividers for the top tier of 7 stowed 81mm mortar rounds. Between the ammo compartments is a seat with a folding back.*

Below: *The side door of the left ammunition compartment is open, showing the four tiers of storage space, with provisions for 7 mortar rounds per tier. The trays and dividers are of welded construction. To the upper left is the left front corner of the machine gun skate rail. (Patton Museum, both)*

Right: *The metal mount for the mortar base plate is viewed through the rear door of the pilot 81mm Mortar Carrier M4 in an Aberdeen Proving Ground photo dated 20 August 1941. The mortar's stock base plate was secured to this mount with the two hinged bars with the locking nuts with handles at the top. On production M4s, the ball mount on the mortar base would be installed directly onto a fixed base plate assembly.*

Below: *An example of an early-production 81mm Mortar Carrier M4, registration number W-4015367, is viewed from the front right with its canvas top installed. The scene was Aberdeen Proving Ground on 25 June 1944. With the mortar and the rear door hidden from view, this vehicle was similar in appearance to a Half-Track Car M2 of the period. "M4" is painted on the cowl. (Patton Museum, both)*

Above: *In a left-rear view of 81mm Mortar Carrier M4 registration number W-4015367, the rear door is visible. Fittings for storing a machine-gun tripod are present to the left of the rear door. Note the flap on the center of the rear panel of the canvas top, with two retainer straps on each side.*

Left: *The rear door of the early-production M4 is open, revealing the 81mm Mortar M1 mounted inside. A grab handle was on each side of the rear armor panel of the body. Above the taillights on each side was a horizontal steel plate with diamond-tread surface. (Patton Museum, both)*

Above: *In this photo of registration number W-4015367, the mortar is set at maximum elevation of +80 degrees, but the muzzle is barely visible above the top of the body of the vehicle. Chalked on the side of the battery box below the side door is "5/9/42," possibly indicating a battery installation on that date. (Patton Museum)*

Below: *The same 81mm Mortar Carrier M4 is seen from above with the door armor lowered, the windshield armor raised, and the mortar at minimum elevation of +40 degrees. At this point, 25 June 1942, the two bins to hold a total of 16 mortar rounds were still in the rear of the vehicle, but later these would be omitted. (Patton Museum)*

Above: *Seen from directly overhead, the same early-production M4 has a .30-caliber machine gun mounted on the front of the skate rail, as well as a front-mounted winch. A radio set and a whip antenna are on top of the right ammunition compartment. Crew seats are between the ammunition bins on each side.*

(Patton Museum) **Below:** *A 9 July 1942 photo from Aberdeen Proving Ground shows a Radio Set SCR-510 and a Mast Base MP-48 as installed in an 81mm Mortar Carrier M4. The equipment is mounted on top of the right ammunition compartment lid, and in the left background is the right front of the cab. (NARA)*

Above: The same SCR-510 set and antenna mast base are seen from a different angle. To the left is the Radio Receiver and Transmitter BC-620-A. To the right is the Plate Supply Unit PE-97, a power-supply unit. Galvin Manufacturing Corporation, Chicago, Illinois, made both pieces of equipment. **Below:** A photo taken for the Armored Force Board at Fort Knox, Kentucky, shows the original arrangement in the rear of the body of a production 81mm Mortar Carrier M4. The view is from between the ammunition compartments facing the rear. At the center, to the immediate rear of the crew seat with the folding back, is the mount for the bottom of the mortar tube. To the far right is the pintle socket for the .30-caliber machine gun. (NARA, both)

Above: *This is the fixed base plate for the mortar tube in a production M4 in its original configuration, viewed from the rear. This fixed plate was called the socket plate, to differentiate it from the portable base plate of the mortar. It was bolted to an angled support, which in turn was bolted to the floor. There were three sockets on the socket plate, similar to the arrangement on the base plate used for firing the mortar on the ground.*

Below: *In its original configuration, the 81mm mortar in the M4 carrier could not be traversed, and its sight was below the top of the body. The M4 in the preceding photos was modified so that the socket plate of the mortar was atop two vertical steel plates, which raised the mortar so that it could be traversed and its sight could protrude above the top of the vehicle's body. (Jim Gilmore collection, both)*

Above: *During experiments with the 81mm mortar mount at Fort Knox, the third method of providing traverse for the weapon is depicted. The socket plate was not of the raised design. The spikes on the bottoms of the bipod legs fit into holes in a curved fixture at the rear of the compartment; two of the holes are visible here. The Armored Force Board deemed this method satisfactory, but this was not the design ultimately approved. (Jim Gilmore collection)* **Below:** *Although the 81mm Mortar Carrier M4 was designed on the principle that normally the mortar would be removed from the vehicle and emplaced on the ground for firing, it soon became evident that it should be possible to fire the mortar from the vehicle. However, the M4 was not optimally designed for this. Thus, following the experiments to improve the ability to fire the mortar from the vehicle, as documented in the preceding photos, the 81mm Mortar Carrier M4A1 was developed, with standardization occurring on 28 January 1943. (ATHS)*

Above: *On the same 81mm Mortar Carrier M4A1 shown in the preceding photo, registration number 40105175, the two storage boxes added to the rear of the body are visible. Retainer straps for bedrolls are on the rears of the boxes. A mine rack is on the side of the body.* **Below:** *The 81mm Mortar Carrier*

M4A1 retained the side doors for the two ammunition compartments to the rear of the cab doors. Below and between the two storage boxes on the rear of the vehicle's body, and overhanging the taillights and the tow pintle, was a three-piece platform supported by diagonal braces. (ATHS, both)

Right: *The upper part of the mortar is visible above the rear door of an 81mm Mortar Carrier M4A1. To the left of the mortar tube is the barrel of a .30-caliber machine gun above the front of the cab. Note the hinged padlock hasps on the lids of the rear storage boxes. (Patton Museum)*

Below: *The nickname "PROWLER" is painted on the driver's door of this 81mm Mortar Carrier M4A1 photographed for the Armored Board at Fort Knox, Kentucky. No U.S. Army registration number is visible. A .30-caliber machine gun is on the front of the skate rail, and to the rear of the gun is a radio antenna. (Kevin Emdee collection)*

Above: *The higher position of the mortar tube on the 81mm Mortar Carrier M4A1, as compared with that of the M4, is apparent from this angle. A dust cover is fitted over the muzzle of the mortar tube. (Kevin Emdee collection)* **Below:** *The following sequence of photos taken on 9 February 1944 at the Ordnance Operation, Engineering Standards Vehicle Laboratory, Detroit, Michigan, documents 81mm Mortar Carrier M4A1 Ordnance Number 1945. A roll of camouflage netting is strapped to the right fender. A dust cover is installed over the winch. Mines are stored on the rack on the side of the body. (Patton Museum)*

Above: *This vehicle had the late-type idler spring. These springs were a modification to the half-tracks following lessons learned in North Africa, where the original, fixed idler spindles were seen to lack the ability to flex with the terrain. A thinner, longer idler spring preceded the later type shown here.* **Below:**

Bedrolls for the six-man crew are strapped to the rear storage boxes. Below the platform between the bottoms of the storage boxes is the portable base plate for the mortar in its travel position. This base plate, designated the type MI, was used when firing the mortar on the ground. (Patton Museum, both)

Above: *The portable base plate for the 81mm Mortar M1 is again seen in its travel position. The platform it is fastened to has two hinges on the right side and a sliding-bolt lock on the left side. Below the base plate is the tow pintle on the rear cross member of the chassis frame.* **Below:** *81mm Mortar Carrier M4A1 Ordnance Number 1945 is seen from the left side on 9 February 1944. Stenciled on the ammunition-compartment door is "PREPARED / BY L.T.D. / 11/28/43 / SCR-509 / SCR-510." The last two lines indicate radio equipment installed. (Patton Museum, both)*

Right: *The same M4AI is viewed from the front. By now, in early 1944, the M4AIs were equipped with the late-type headlight assemblies, which were removable and included a marker light attached to the top of each of the service-headlight housings. Protecting the lights were form-fitting brush guards, different in design than the early, grille-type brush guards. (Patton Museum)*

Below: *With the left side of the hood of an 81mm Mortar Carrier M4AI open, the White Model 160AX in-line engine is visible inside. To the left is the radiator. On the side of the front of the engine is the water pump. At the upper center of the engine is the distributor. To the right is the surge tank. (Patton Museum)*

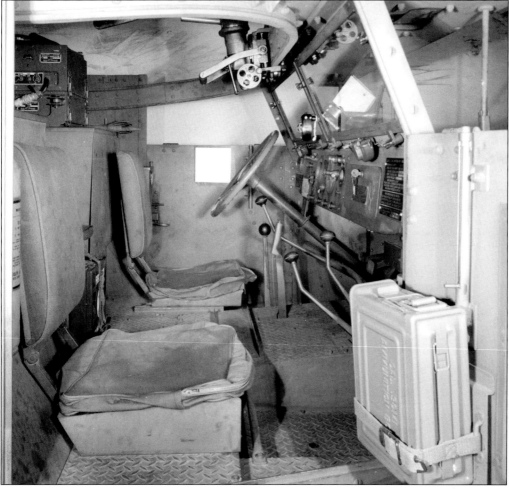

Above: The right side of the engine of an 81mm Mortar Carrier M4A1 is shown. To the left is the oil-bath air cleaner, from which an air hose runs to the carburetor. Below and adjacent to the carb is the manifold, with the White logo and part number, 322570, marked on it. To the right is the oil filter. (Patton Museum)

Left: The cab of M4A1 Ordnance Number 1945 is viewed through the right door. On a holder on the inside of the door is a 30-caliber ammunition box. To the left, on the left 81mm ammunition compartment is a radio set. To the upper center, mounted on the skate rail, is the carriage for the machine gun, fitted with rollers to enable it to be positioned as desired around the skate rail. The small wheel with four holes in it, toward the bottom of the carriage, is the canting wheel, for cross-leveling the carriage. (Patton Museum)

Above: *In another of the 9 February 1944 photos from the Engineering Standards Vehicle Laboratory in Detroit, an 81mm Mortar M1 is seen through the open door at the rear of an 81mm Mortar Carrier M4A1. The fixed socket plate of the mortar is on a raised platform bolted to the floor. In the foreground is the base for the mortar bipod legs, with holes for securing the spikes at the bottoms of the legs and to allow for traversing the mortar by repositioning the legs.* **Below:** *The interior layout of an 81mm Mortar Carrier M4A1 is seen from above. The two rear 81mm ammunition bins flanking the mortar were discontinued with the M4A1. In addition to two seats in the cab, there are two crew seats, arranged back-to-back, between the ammunition compartments, and two inward-facing seats to the sides of the fuel tanks. Radio equipment is on top of both ammunition compartments. At the rear of the compartment is the support for the mortar bipod, with holes arranged in a radius on it to engage the spikes on the tripod legs. (Patton Museum, both)*

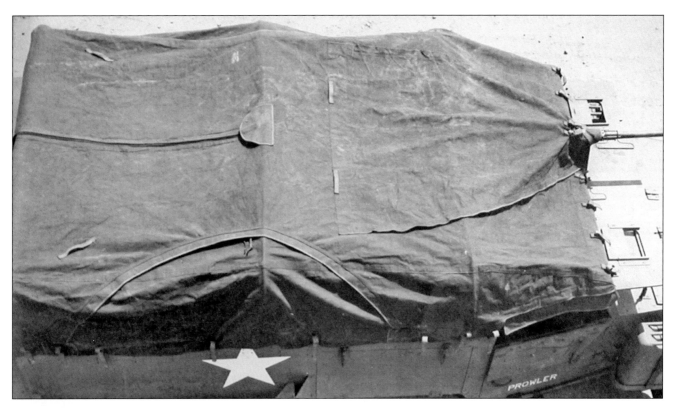

Above: *The canvas top of an 81mm Mortar Carrier M4A1 is seen from above, with all flaps fully closed and secured. This vehicle is "PROWLER," during analysis by the Armored Force Board at Fort Knox, Kentucky. The canvas cover, officially referred to as the top, was supported by three removable bows, and the front of the top was attached to the top of the windshield frame. The top was secured with straps to footman loops* attached to the body and the windshield frame. **Below:** *The same vehicle is shown with all of the flaps of the top open. These included side flaps, a front flap to allow operation of the machine gun, and a rear flap to permit firing the mortar without completely removing the canvas top. The rear flap actually had two panels, joined at the front-to-rear centerline of the canvas top with a zipper. (Jim Gilmore collection, both)*

Above: *An M4A1 without the canvas top fitted is seen from the left side. The seat facing to the rear toward the mortar has been tilted to the rear, revealing a stowage space below it. There also was a stowage space under the floor to the rear of the mortar socket plate. Three canteens are stored on each of the fuel*

tanks. **Below:** *The same vehicle is now seen with the full crew of six men seated in it. Conditions appear to be somewhat cramped, but the M4A1 was much less crowded than the M4, in part due to the removal of the two rear ammunition bins that had been present in the M4. (Jim Gilmore collection, both)*

Troops using the M4 and M4A1 mortar carriers in maneuvers and combat reported that the rear-firing mortar configuration of those vehicles was not the best all-around arrangement for effective use of the 81mm mortar. Thus, the Armored Force Board began investigating a better way to mount the mortar on the half-track and developed the 81mm Mortar Carrier T19. An example is shown here with the mortar not installed. The skate rail was replaced by a pedestal for a machine gun in the rear of the vehicle. Flanking the pedestal are two forward-facing seats. To the front of the pedestal is the fixed socket plate for the mortar. (ATHS)

The 81mm Mortar Carrier T19 incorporated a drastic revamping of the 81mm mortar ammunition storage. The ammunition compartments with the top lids and side doors, which dated back to the M2 half-track, were omitted in favor of open-topped, vertically positioned ammunition bins. New fuel tanks were installed. The seating also was rearranged, with three seats to the front, one facing inward to the rear of the ammo bins behind the driver's seat, and two forward-facing seats at the rear. (ATHS)

Above: The interior stowage arrangements in an 81mm Mortar Carrier T19 are documented in an Aberdeen Proving Ground photograph dated 8 June 1943. Toward the right are the right fuel tank, the radio rack, and the radio antenna mount. Cased mortar rounds are stored in the bins. Details of the .50-caliber machine gun barrel and the mortar's traversing mechanism are also in view. (Jim Gilmore collection)

Below: The seating arrangements for the crew of the 81mm Mortar Carrier T19 are depicted in this photo of a vehicle undergoing analysis by the Armored Force Board Test Operation at Fort Knox, Kentucky. There was considerably more space for the crewmen in the fighting compartment than in the Half-Track 81mm Mortar Carriers M4 and M4A1, although the cab was crowded. (Jim Gilmore collection)

A crew demonstrates loading the mortar in an 81mm Mortar Carrier T19; the loader is about to drop a round into the tube. A .50-caliber machine gun is mounted on the pedestal. A full complement of mortar rounds are loaded in the bins. The portable mortar base plate is stored on the rear door between the bedrolls. (Jim Gilmore collection)

Above: The Armored Force Board at Fort Knox views stowage arrangements in the 81mm Mortar Carrier T19 from above the right side of the vehicle during tests. Mortar ammunition in fiberboard packing tubes is stored to the sides and front of the mortar, with some rounds being stored horizontally to the front of the base plate of the mortar. The seats in the fighting compartment were hinged and are shown folded forward, revealing the stowage compartments underneath them. **Below:** The same 81mm Mortar Carrier T19 undergoing tests by the Armored Board has the canvas top installed, and the roof panels could be unzipped and rolled up without removing the entire top. Note the radio set to the front of the right fuel tank and the individual covers over the mortar ammunition bins. The registration number on the hood is 40138751. (Jim Gilmore collection, both)

Above: *The top of the 81mm Mortar Carrier T19 has been unrolled and pulled over the fighting compartment, and the slits for the machine gun and the mortar and the side slit have been left open. Mines are stowed on the rack on the side of the vehicle. (Jim Gilmore collection)* **Below:** *The 81mm Mortar Carrier T19 was standardized as the 81mm Mortar Carrier M21 on 7 June 1943. White produced these vehicles for a total run of 110* vehicles, delivering them to the Army from January to March 1944. The M21 included ladder-shaped storage racks on the side of the body, similar to those used on the Half-Track Cars M3A2 and M5A2. This example, Ordnance Number 25 and registration number 40172936, was photographed for the Ordnance Operation, Engineering Standards Vehicle Laboratory, Detroit, Michigan on 28 April 1944. (Patton Museum)*

Above: *In another view of M21 USA Number 40172936, a machine gun tripod is strapped to the rear of the fender. Bows to support the canvas top are strapped to the mine rack. A stencil on the side of the body to the rear of the driver's door indicates that SCR-509 and SCR-510 radio sets were installed. (Patton Museum)*

Below: *Two folding stowage racks were installed on the rear of the 81mm Mortar Carrier M21, of the type used on the M3A2 and M5A2 personnel-carrier half-tracks. On each side of each rack was a hinged support bar, not to be confused with the straps running from the bedrolls to footman loops near the top of the body. (Patton Museum)*

Left: *In a frontal view of 81mm Mortar Carrier M21 registration number 40172936, the muzzle of the mortar, the .50-caliber machine gun, and the antenna protrude above the top of the vehicle. Note the beveled-bottom ammunition box for the machine gun. (Patton Museum)*

Below: *The left side of the engine compartment of M21 registration number 40172936 is displayed. The engine in the M21 remained the White Model 160AX, a 6-cylinder, 4-cycle, inline design with a displacement of 386 cubic inches. The label on the surge tank warns to never remove the surge-tank cap, as the radiator cap was to be used for filling, and that the radiator cap should never be removed while the engine is hot. (Patton Museum)*

Above: *The right side of the same engine is shown in an 11 April 1944 photo. To the far right is the FRAM oil filter. To the left is the oil-bath air cleaner. In the middle are the carburetor, exhaust manifold, oil filler pipe, and dipstick. (Patton Museum)*

Right: *The cab of M21 registration number 40172936 is shown. Strapped to the door is a binocular case, above which is the holder assembly for the folding top of the door. The seat-cushion shells had zippers on the fronts; folded blankets were stuffed in them to form the cushions. The center seat is higher than and slightly to the rear of the other two front seats. (Patton Museum)*

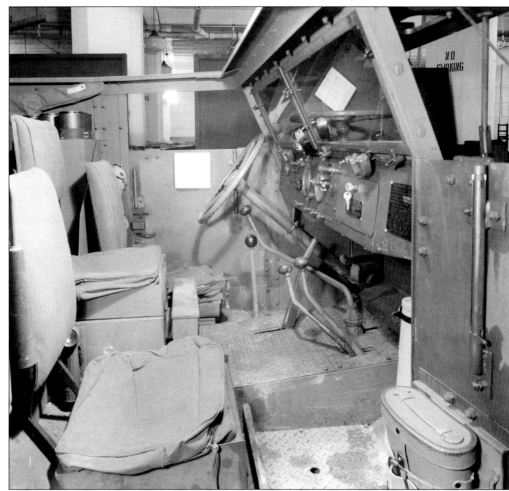

Above: *The interior of the fighting compartment of M21 registration number 40172936 is viewed from above the cab. A full complement of 81mm mortar rounds in fiberboard packing tubes is in the bins, with extra rounds stacked on the floor. Below the radio antenna and to the front of the right fuel tank is a rack for radio equipment, complete with zippered canvas dust covers. (Patton Museum)*

Left: *The interior of an 81mm Mortar Carrier M21 is seen from the rear. To the lower right, a canvas cover with a tightening strap is over the antenna base. At the lower center is the pintle socket on top of the machine-gun pedestal. Between the large and the small ammo bins to the left is a seatback. The legs of the mortar bipod are attached to a base that could be moved to the left or the right on a curved track, to traverse the piece. (Patton Museum)*

Above: *The canvas top of an M21 is installed and is observed from above. There are two triangular flaps on the roof of the top, for opening it to fire the mortar and the machine gun. The flap for the mortar is partially open and folded forward; the zippers for this flap extend all the way to the front end of the top. A separate dust cover is installed on the .50-caliber machine gun.*

Below: *81mm Mortar Carrier M21 Ordnance Number 25 and registration number 40172936 is viewed from overhead without the top installed, giving a clear idea of the seating and ammunition-storage arrangements and the amount of space available for the crew to serve the mortar. (Patton Museum, both)*

Above: *In its attempts in the 1930s to provide greater mobility for its mortars, the Army experimented with the 4.2-inch Mortar Motor Carriage T2, based on a small tracked vehicle with four bogie wheels per side. The mortar, situated in the front of the vehicle, is depressed so that the tube is not visible. An example is shown in a 23 May 1935 photograph following an eight-hour run. Developed for the U.S. Army's Chemical Warfare Service, the 4.2-inch chemical mortar was based on the British Stokes mortar of* World War I and was designed to fire rounds containing poisonous gas. **Below:** *The mortar is elevated on this 4.2-inch Mortar Motor Carriage T2 assigned to Company A of the 2nd Separate Chemical Mortar Battalion, showing its position in the forward end of the vehicle, at or around the center of the longitudinal centerline of the vehicle. To the rear of the driver is the engine compartment, with a louvered side door open. (U.S. Army Chemical Corps Museum, both)*

Above: Two G.I.s take a break at the front of a 4.2-inch Mortar Motor Carriage T2 during a field exercise. A service headlight was on each fender, and a horn or siren was on the left fender.
Below: In 1938, the Rock Island Arsenal converted six White Scout Cars M3 to carriers for the 4.2-inch chemical mortar.

These were designated the 4.2-inch Motor Mortar Carriage T5E1. The mortar was on a folding mount that was extended to the rear of the vehicle, as shown here, for emplacement. This photo was taken at Rock Island Arsenal on 17 June 1938. (U.S. Army Chemical Corps Museum, both)

Above: *The mortar of a 4.2-inch Motor Mortar Carriage T5E1 has been deployed to the rear of the modified Scout Car M3. Note the rails extending from the rear of the vehicle, part of the mechanism for deploying and transporting the mortar.* **Below:**

The White 4.2-inch Motor Mortar Carriage T5E1 is disposed for travel in this Rock Island Arsenal photograph dated 17 June 1938. The vehicle's canvas top is installed and its registration number is W-60549. (U.S. Army Chemical Corps Museum, both)

Above: White 4.2-inch Motor Mortar Carriage T5E1 U.S. Army registration number W-60549 is viewed from the right side with the canvas top removed. The bows are stored upside-down on the ledge above the rear wheel. The upper, telescoping tube of the pedestal mount next to the door has a bright, bare-metal finish. On the cowl next to the pedestal are a spotlight and a collapsible bucket in a holder. (U.S. Army Chemical Corps Museum)

Right: One of the six White 4.2-inch Motor Mortar Carriages T5E1 is seen from above at Rock Island Arsenal with the mortar in the travel position. The mortar tube is pointing forward, and the mortar's base plate is resting in an upright position at the rear of the fighting compartment. Two rearward-facing upholstered seats flank the mortar tube. (U.S. Army Chemical Corps Museum)

Below: Members of the Mortar Platoon of the 2nd Separate Chemical Mortar Battalion demonstrate serving their 4.2-inch Motor Mortar Carriages T5E1. The mortars have been hauled out of the vehicles and are on the ground. (U.S. Army Chemical Corps Museum)

Above: *In 1942 Aberdeen Proving Ground commenced a project to determine the feasibility of mounting a 4.2-inch mortar on a standard half-track. Experiments were conducted with the mortar on an M4 mortar carrier and, as shown in this photo dated 30 December 1942, a Half-Track Car M3. Stowage provisions for 32 rounds of 4.2-inch ammunition were included. During the early part of the U.S. involvement in World War II, the Chemical Warfare Service authorized its troops to begin using high-explosive rounds in its 4.2-inch mortars. (Patton Museum)*

Right: *In the experimental 4.2-inch mortar installation in an M4 half-track, the mortar was emplaced on a small socket plate on a raised base on the floor of the fighting compartment. A two-inch rubber pad was sandwiched between the socket plate and the base to buffer the recoil, as shown in a 15 September 1942 photograph. (Patton Museum)*

Right: *Despite the use of a 2-inch rubber buffer on the mortar base on the experimental installation in the M4 half-track, the firing of the mortar damaged the socket plate and the support structure underneath the mortar. This 21 September 1942 photo documents bending of the socket plate after 15 rounds had been fired. (Patton Museum)*

Below: *By early 1943, the focus had changed to the Half-Track Car M3A1 as the platform for the 4.2-inch mortar. The resulting vehicle was designated the 4.2-inch Chemical Mortar Carrier T21. The mortar was arranged to fire to the rear, and, as seen in this 25 May 1943 photo and the following one, from most angles there was little visual evidence to differentiate this vehicle from a stock Half-Track Car M3A1. (NARA via Dana Bell)*

Above: *The 4.2-inch Chemical Mortar Carrier T21 was configured to carry 90 4.2-inch mortar rounds as well as 400 rounds of .50-caliber and 2,000 rounds of .30-caliber ammunition. A folding storage rack was on the left rear of the vehicle and a stowage box on the right rear. (NARA via Dana Bell)*

Left: *The effort to produce a rear-firing 4.2-inch Chemical Mortar on a Half-Track Personnel Carrier M3A1 was known as Project No. 6-3-2 of Ordnance Program 5550, conducted from December 1942 to August 1943, and it was this project that yielded the 4.2-inch Chemical Mortar Carrier T21. One of the determinations arrived at from tests under this program was that the main cross member of the chassis frame, over which the mortar base plate was mounted, was insufficiently strong to stand the shock of firing. Also, the test report called for changing the orientation of the mortar to fire to the front, but to achieve this, it would be necessary to remove the machine gun ring mount. This view of a T21 was taken for inclusion in the report of Ordnance Program 5550 at Aberdeen Proving Ground on 25 May 1943. (NARA via Dana Bell)*

Above: *In a 26 March 1943 photograph from Aberdeen Proving Ground, a soldier demonstrates the accessibility of an SCR-521 radio to the driver of a 4.2-inch Chemical Mortar Carrier T21. He could adjust the controls of the radio while driving by reaching backwards with his right hand. The G.I. is wearing headphones and a throat microphone set. (Jim Gilmore collection)*

Right: *The cab of a 4.2-inch Chemical Mortar Carrier T21 is viewed through the driver's door in a photo taken for Project 6-3-2 at Aberdeen Proving Ground on 25 May 1943. One of the tasks of this project was to devise a list and placement locations of equipment and supplies particular to this type of vehicle, and to left of the driver's seat is a demountable box for storing 18 30-round magazines for .45-caliber submachine gun ammunition and 540 rounds of that ammunition. (NARA via Dana Bell)*

Left: *In a rear view of a 4.2-inch Chemical Mortar Carrier T21, the positioning of the mortar in the extreme rear of the fighting compartment is apparent. Four ammunition-storage compartments are in view. A radio set is to the rear of the driver's seat. In addition to the ring mount, there was a socket for a pintle mount for a .30-caliber machine gun atop each side of the fighting compartment. (Patton Museum)*

Right: *The same 4.2-inch Chemical Mortar Carrier T21 is seen from the left front. As occurred with the M4 and M4A1 mortar carriers, the rearward orientation of the mortar limited the vehicle's effectiveness in combat, requiring the driver to orient the vehicle with its rear to the enemy before firing, thus extending reaction times. (Patton Museum)*

Right: *An SCR-510 radio was located in a rack next to the left fuel tank in the 4.2-inch Chemical Mortar T21, as shown in a photo taken for Project No. 6-3-2 at Aberdeen Proving Ground on 25 May 1943. The box over the left fuel tank to the front of the antenna held one detachable headlight assembly and one detachable blackout lamp. Although hidden in the shadows, there is a .45-caliber Thompson submachine gun stored on the side of the body above the left fuel tank. (NARA via Dana Bell)*

Left: *Stowage provisions in a 4.2-inch Chemical Mortar Carrier T21 are depicted in a photograph taken for Project no. 6-3-2 at Aberdeen Proving Ground on 25 May 1943. The base plate of the mortar is at the bottom center. To the left are the radio and antenna installations. Below the ring mount are bins for two .50-caliber ammunition boxes and four .30-caliber ammunition boxes. Stowed over the fuel tank to the left is a machine-gun tripod. (NARA via Dana Bell)*

Above: *The 4.2-inch Chemical Mortar Carrier T21E1 placed the mortar in a forward-firing position, as seen in a photo stamped 10 March 1944. This required the omitting the ring mount and pulpit. Open-topped, divided bins for 4.2-inch ammunition were provided: there were two forward bins for 32 rounds each and, to the fronts of the fuel tanks, two bins for 9 rounds each. Between the large bins and the small bins on each side was an inward-facing crew seat. Toward the rear of the fighting compartment was a .50-caliber machine gun on a pedestal mount.* **Below:** *The base of the 4.2-inch mortar of the T21E2 carrier rested on a special socket plate that was bolted to an X-shaped casting mounted on the chassis frame. At the bottom are the two large ammo bins; to the top are the smaller, 9-round ammunition bins. (NARA via Dana Bell, both)*

Above: *A 4.2-inch Chemical Mortar Carrier T21E1 is viewed from the left rear in a photo stamped 10 March 1944, showing the arrangement of the folding storage racks on the rear, the rail-type storage racks on the side, and the mine rack. Also in view are the radio antenna and its mount and the pedestal-mounted .50-caliber machine gun.* **Below:** *Conducted from March to April 1944, Project No. 3560/6-3-5 of the Ordnance Research Center at Aberdeen Proving Ground was focused on designing and testing an improved, forward-firing 4.2-inch Chemical Mortar mount to supplant the rear-firing 4.2-inch*

Chemical Mortar Carrier T21. In this project, the chassis frame under the mortar base plate was strengthened; the ring mount was removed, and a pedestal mount for a .50-caliber machine gun was installed in the fighting compartment; and, ultimately, a sheet-metal top was devised for the cab to prevent blast damage to the instruments. This vehicle, designated the 4.2-inch Chemical Mortar Carrier T21E1, is shown in the early part of the project, at Aberdeen on 10 March 1944. The tarpaulin is installed, and the sheet-metal top was yet to be devised. (NARA via Dana Bell, both)

Above: *The same T21E1 is seen without the tarpaulin installed. This vehicle was assigned U.S. Army registration number 40182725. The pedestal-mounted machine gun and a radio antenna base unit are visible above the top of the fighting compartment, but there is no sign of the forward-firing 4.2-inch chemical mortar from this angle.*
Below: *These 13 March 1944 photographs were taken to*

document the radio antenna base unit and mount during tests at Aberdeen Proving Ground under Project No. 3560/6-3-5. In the lower part of the photograph to the left and in the photo to the right, the associated radio set is visible. The photo on the right also reveals some details of the mortar mount and the mortar ammunition bins. (NARA via Dana Bell, both)

Above: *This photo, taken on 18 March 1944, documents damage to the instrument panel of the T21E1 from the blast of the 4.2-inch mortar when firing at minimum depression of 42 degrees during Project 3560/6-3-5 tests. All of the glass lenses of the instruments were shattered; the tachometer needle, the panel light shade, and the nomenclature plate were blown away; and the starter switch and the ammeter were destroyed.*
Below: *By 18 April 1944, the Ordnance Research Center had* arrived at a solution to the problem of blast damage to the instrument panel in the form of a sheet metal top for the cab. The top photo shows the top from the right side of the vehicle. Note the reinforcing ribs on the rear panel of the top. The bottom photo shows the top from the rear; it included a recess in the upper rear corner of the top to provide clearance for the mortar at its lowest elevation. (NARA via Dana Bell)*

The 4.2-inch chemical mortar in a T2IEI carrier is seen from the rear. The piece is traversed 250 mils left, which was the extreme left traverse. At the top of the photo is the rear of an experimental metal cab cover. (U.S. Army Chemical Corps Museum)

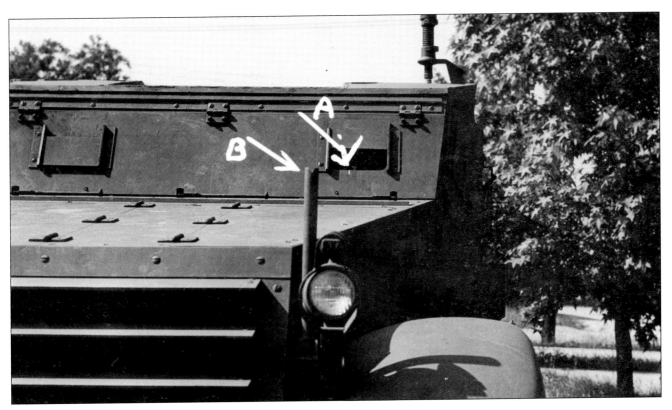

Above: *Aids for helping the driver align the T21E1 chemical mortar carrier with the target are documented in this photo. "A" indicates a white mark on the driver's vision slot, and "B" is a holder for an aiming stake.* **Below:** *The legs of the 4.2-inch mortar rested on sliding bearings in a slightly curved slot at the front of the fighting compartment. Sliding the bipod from side to side in this manner resulted in a traverse of 125 mils to either side of the longitudinal centerline of the vehicle. Operating the mortar's traversing screw added another 125 mils to the right and left traverse of the piece, yielding a total possible traverse of 250 mils to the right or left. (U.S. Army Chemical Corps Museum)*

Above: *Crewmen have dismounted a 4.2-inch chemical mortar from its socket plate (lower left) in a T21E1 carrier in order to remove a misfired round. The presence of the armored roof over the cab (right) prevented the crew from extracting the round in the normal manner.* **Below:** *The same mortar crew has turned the tube to the rear and lowered the muzzle end, from which the misfired round is emerging. In the foreground are uncased mortar rounds, stored with their bases pointing up. The square objects attached to the projectile bases are incremental propelling charges, called disks. The mortar rounds had a built-in charge which yielded a maximum range of about 340 yards. By attaching incremental disks to the base of the round, the range could be extended to up to 4,400 yards. (U.S. Army Chemical Corps Museum, both)*

Right: *Despite the newly designed socket plate and support structure for the 4.2-inch mortar on the T21E1 carrier, this mount was not without its teething problems. This photo documents how a metal cup designed to cradle the socket plate had moved approximately two inches from the firing of the mortar. The lines and arrows indicate the range of movement. (U.S. Army Chemical Corps Museum)*

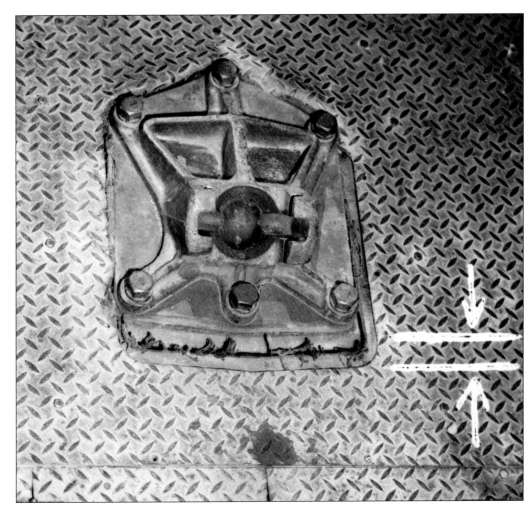

Below: *In a view of the top of the metal cab cover of a T21E1 mortar carrier, the arrows indicate where minor cracks had developed around welds after firing the 4.2-inch mortar with 25½ rings of M6 propelling charge. To the left is the antenna base and bracket, and in the background is the front of the hood of the half-track. (U.S. Army Chemical Corps Museum)*

Above: *In a side view of the left side of the cab of a T21E1 mortar carrier, the arrow indicates a slight crack in a weld bead in the metal top after the mortar had been firing rounds with 25½ rings of M6 propelling charge. The weld was where the metal top was attached to the top of the A-column.* **Below:** *The portable base plate for the 4.2-inch mortar was stored for travel in a special steel rack attached to the bottom of the rear of the chassis frame of the T21E1 mortar carrier. (U.S. Army Chemical Corps Museum, both)*

Crewmen are serving the 4.2-inch chemical mortar on a T2IEI mortar carrier equipped with a metal cab cover. To the left side of the fighting compartment are cased mortar rounds; to the right are uncased rounds, stored with the base end up. In the distance, the letters A and C indicate aiming stakes the driver aligned the vehicle with, and B indicates an aiming stake the gunner is using as a reference point for aiming the piece. (U.S. Army Chemical Corps Museum)

Chapter 2:
Gun Motor Carriages

The T12 and T48

As war engulfed both Europe and the Pacific, it became apparent to the leadership that the U.S. Army was sorely lacking in self-propelled artillery vehicles. Not only was there a need to develop and place into production specialized vehicles of this type, it was felt that as a stop-gap measure it would be prudent to marry existing guns to vehicles already in production.

Such marriage was suggested at a 25 June 1941 conference of the Assistant Chief of Staff, G-3 and the Ordnance Department, held at Aberdeen Proving Ground. As a result of this, an initiative was begun to mount a 75mm gun on the M3 Personnel Carrier half-track.

The resultant gun motor carriage would make the best use of the existing stocks of 75mm guns, crating a substitute weapon for use by a provisional tank destroyer unit during the forthcoming autumn maneuvers.

The gun selected was the 75mm gun M1897A4, itself a modernized version of the famed M1897 "French 75" which gained notoriety during WWI. The gun was to be mounted to fire forward over the hood of the halftrack, and it was to be served from within the vehicle. The M1897A4 was typically mounted on the 75mm gun carriage M2A3, a relatively modern two-wheel, split-trail carriage with pneumatic tires. The range of elevation was -9 to 49 degrees, with a 30-degree left and right traverse. Maximum range of the weapon, firing an APC round, was 13,870 yards, and muzzle velocity was

2,000 feet per second. The round could defeat 2.5-inches of homogenous armor plate at 1,000 yards.

The Adjutant General approved the marriage of this gun, with mount and shield made by Parrish Pressed Steel Company, with the M3 half-track on 3 July 1941. Personnel at Aberdeen Proving Ground set out to construct the pilot of the new vehicle, by then given the designation T12.

For the pilot, a special base was fabricated which replaced the wheels, trails and remaining lower assembly of the conventional gun carriage. The upper portion of the traditional gun carriage was retained however, and was affixed to the new base.

The half-track itself was modified, and the armored windshield covers were configured to fold down rather than the standard upward travel, while the conventional glass windshield panels were dispensed with entirely. A notch was cut in the upper center of the windshield armor in order to accommodate the gun being lowered and locked in the travel position.

In the fighting compartment even more extensive changes were made. The rear seats, fuel tanks, gun racks and subfloor were removed. In their place were installed new fuel tanks located at the rear of the fighting compartment and a new subfloor installed that would accommodate ten four-round boxes of 75mm ammunition as well as one box of machine gun ammo.

The pilot vehicle was demonstrated at Aberdeen on 16 July 1941, with the demonstration going well enough that authorization was given to procure 36

On 27 October 1941, the 75mm Gun Motor Carriage T12 is viewed from the front. Note the V-shaped notch in the top center of the armored windshield to accommodate the bottom of the recoil mechanism of the 75mm gun. (Jim Gilmore collection)

further examples for service test.

These vehicles would differ slightly from the pilot, drawing on the experience of the testing for improvements. Notable among these was increasing the crew from four to five, providing stowage for 19 additional 75mm rounds in the lower part of the gun mount, and relocating the machine gun. But the most significant change was the redesign of the gun shield in order to provide protection against .30-caliber armor-piercing ammunition at 250 yards.

The first 36 vehicles were tested at Aberdeen Proving Ground, and also by the 93rd Antitank Battalion at Fort Meade, Maryland. As a result of those tests, the military characteristics were revised slightly, and on 21 November 1941 the vehicle was standardized as the 75mm Gun Motor Carriage M3.

However, in a report dated 22 December 1941, the Armored Force Board stated that the vehicle was not completely satisfactory and should be used only as a guide toward creating a more satisfactory mount. However, it was noted that the T12/M3 could be used until such a more suitable mount was constructed, commenting "The 75-mm Gun Motor Carriage, T12, although not completely satisfactory as a self-propelled Field Artillery weapon, has served to demonstrate some of the advantages and disadvantages of a self-propelled mount. The principal advantages demonstrated from this test are that the self-propelled mounts can occupy firing position more rapidly than towed guns, and that self-propelled mounts can leave a firing position more rapidly than a towed gun. Self-propelled mounts and towed guns possess the same degree of rapidity in initial laying and control in the firing battery. For direct laying, self-propelled mounts can be placed in firing position almost instantaneously. For indirect fire, they can be placed in firing position in less than one-fourth of the time required for towed guns."

While many official U.S. Government as well as surviving Autocar documents agree that 2,202 T12/M3 Gun Motor Carriages were produced, their contract numbers and quantities are a bit less clear.

Autocar records indicate that there were some T12 vehicles among the half-tracks procured on contract W-670-ORD-6276. However, the Summary Report of Tank and Combat Vehicle acceptances, corrected to April 1946, lists 36 vehicles as ordered on production order T-1915, contract W-670-ORD-1796, while 50 of the gun motor carriages were on production order T-2052 of the same contract.

Regardless of distribution between these contracts and their numbers, it is likely that the vehicles mentioned above were ordnance serial numbers 1 through 86, and bore registration numbers 409528 thru 409613. Sixty-one of these vehicles were delivered in August 1941, and 25 in September of that year.

The May 1945 edition of the Ordnance Department, Armored, Tank and Combat Vehicles 1940-1945 lists that contract W-670-ORD-1765 production order T-3042 was for 1,350 of the Gun Motor Carriages with serial numbers 87 through 1436, registration numbers 4017060 through 4018409. These vehicles were delivered between February 1942 and the end of the year. The same document notes that subsequently production order T-13054 was issued for 1,247 of these completed vehicles to be converted to M3A1 personnel carriers.

Interestingly, the Summary Report of Tank and Combat Vehicle acceptances, corrected to April 1946, indicates that the 1,350 vehicles on production order T-3042 were divided between contracts 1765 and 6290. Of note, these 1,350 vehicles were all originally ordered as M3 personnel carriers; 741 on production order T-544, contract W-741-ORD-6290 and 609 and on production order T-1684, but a change order was issued to that contract, prior to the vehicles being produced, directing that they be completed as gun motor carriages instead. Autocar's ledgers list the gun motor carriages on contract W-670-ORD-6290 as M3-75 vehicles, as opposed to the T12 designation used by the company in reference to the 86 vehicles diverted from contract W-670-ORD-6276 for conversion to gun motor carriages. Both contracts were issued in September 1940.

Thus, 1,350 vehicles were initially ordered as

Above: *Three of the U.S. Army's half-track mobile artillery vehicles are showcased in this Aberdeen Proving Ground photo from 25 June 1943. From left to right they are: a 75mm Howitzer Motor Carriage T30; a 105mm Howitzer Motor Carriage T19; and a 75mm Gun Motor Carriage M3. All three types would see active service in World War II. (Patton Museum)*

Below: *Drawing on lessons learned from the German Blitzkrieg of 1940, the U.S. Army began looking for ways to strengthen its antitank forces in 1941. The idea was to mount antitank guns on lightly armored, highly mobile vehicles, making up in mobility and firepower for what was sacrificed in protection. An early project concerned mounting a 75mm Gun M1897A4 on a Carrier, Personnel, Half-Track M3 to form the 75mm Gun Motor Carriage T12, an example of which is shown at Aberdeen Proving Ground on 21 July 1941. (NARA)*

personnel carriers, a change order was issued and they were built as gun motor carriages, and a subsequent contract issued to convert 1,247 of them into the personnel carriers as they were originally ordered!

The May 1945 edition of the Ordnance Department, Armored, Tank and Combat Vehicles 1940-1945 also lists contract W-670-ORD-2597 production order T-4163 for 626 units, serial numbers 1467 through 2092, registration numbers 4053724 through 4054349, while the Summary Report of Tank and Combat Vehicle acceptances, corrected to April 1946, indicates that this production order was for 736 units.

Both documents list W-670-ORD-2597 production order T-4073 for 30 units, with Ordnance Department, Armored, Tank and Combat vehicles listing serial numbers 1437 through 1466, and registration numbers 4053350 through 4053379 for these M3-75s.

The Summary Report of Tank and Combat Vehicles indicates that the 766 vehicles it lists on contract W-670-ORD-2597 were delivered in 1943, which corresponds to the entries listed both Autocar's ledger listing of deliveries to the U.S. Government for 1943 as well as the Chief of Ordnances report "Recapitulation of Facility Expansions for Tracked and Wheeled Vehicles from 1940 to July 15 1945."

As with the 1942 production, a later production order, T-11019, was issued to cover the conversion of 113 of the 1943-produced M3-75 gun motor carriages into M3A1 personnel carriers.

There exists an Aberdeen Proving Ground report covering the favorable testing of a 75mm Gun Motor Carriage using the M2A2 carriage, 75mm mount M5 rather than the M2A3 carriage in the 75mm Gun Motor Carriage.

Due to concerns that a shortage of the M2A3 carriages would impede the production of the M3-75 Gun Motor Carriage and the desire for a substitute, the Ordnance Committee in July 1942 assigned the designation 75mm Gun Motor Carriage M3A1 to the vehicle when equipped with the M2A2 carriage rather than the M2A3. Testing of this

arrangement at Aberdeen in January 1943 went well.

However, with the exception of three photos of the test article, no photographs of an M3A1 75mm Gun Motor Carriage have been observed by this author. Further, despite the excruciating details provided in the original source documents cited throughout this narrative, there is no reference anywhere to production of the M3A1 75mm Gun Motor Carriages, but for a single sentence in the Record of Developmental and Experimental Ordnance dated 6 December 1944. This leads the author to the opinion that only the single test article was created.

The same Record of Developmental and Experimental Ordnance dated 6 December 1944 also includes a sentence stating that "the 75-mm Gun Motor Carriage M3 was supplied to the British under the Lend-Lease program and was one of the "secret weapons" which helped push back Marshal Rommel's troops in Africa."

While it is possible that some of the M3-75s were provided to the Commonwealth through field transfers, the authoritative "Lend-Lease Shipments World War II," prepared by the War Department and issued 31 December 1946 lists no Lend-Lease shipments of the T12 or M3-75 to the Commonwealth, or any other nation.

As a result of the U.S. Army fielding better tank destroyers, in March 1944 the M3-75 was reclassified as Limited Standard by OCM 23202, and on 9 August of that year the Ordnance Committee recommended that the vehicles be declared obsolete and the chassis converted to M3A1 personnel carriers.

T73 75mm Gun Motor Carriage

As previously noted, the M3-75 was armed with M1897A4 75mm guns drawn from existing army stocks. In early 1943, with the perception that half-track based tank destroyers would remain in production for some time, and dwindling inventories of the M1897A4, an alternate weapon was sought.

Attention turned to arming the half-track with the 75mm M3 gun, as used in the M4 Sherman medium tank. Authorization was granted in March

Above: *The pilot 75mm Gun Motor Carriage T12 is viewed from the right side during trials at Aberdeen. ("Gun Motor Carriage" often is abbreviated as GMC.) Personnel at Aberdeen Proving Ground under the direction of Maj. Robert J. Icks performed the conversion of an M3 half-track to the pilot 75mm GMC T12, and an initial production lot of 86 T12s were produced in August and September 1941. The pilot T12 lacked a windshield and the frames above the doors to support it. Protruding above the rear part of the fighting compartment is the top of a pedestal mount for an antiaircraft machine gun. (NARA)*

Below: *After the pilot 75mm Gun Motor Carriage T12, subsequent T12s were equipped with an armored windshield, hinged at the bottom to allow for free movement of the 75mm gun, as well as frames above the cab doors to support the windshield when it was in the raised position. The gun shield, the same as used on the towed version of the gun, had two braces to the front and a notch on top of the right side of the shield for the gunner's sight. (NARA)*

1943 to design and produce an experimental sleigh and modifying the gun such that it and 75mm gun recoil mechanism M2 could be mounted on a half-track, much like the M3-75.

The modified gun was designated T15, the 75mm gun mount the T17, and the new gun motor carriage the T73.

However, even as the prototype was being assembled at Aberdeen, the decision had been made that no further 75mm-armed half-tracks would be produced. Thus, only preliminary testing of the sole example was undertaken by the Proving Ground. While the brief report indicated that the T73 was largely satisfactory, further refinement, particularly regarding clearances between the weapon and the vehicle, would be needed before placing the vehicle in production.

T48 57mm Gun Motor Carriage

Drawing on the success of the T12/M3-75, on 15 April 1942 the development of a similar vehicle armed with the M1 57mm gun was recommended by OCM 18099. The M1 was a U.S.-produced version of the British 6-pounder Mark V. The new vehicle was designated T48.

Technicians at Aberdeen Proving Ground constructed the pilot in early 1942, mounting the gun and M12 recoil mechanism on a tubular pedestal, including the top portion of the M1 field carriage. Soon enough, the original pedestal was replaced by a new conical design, which was designated the 57mm gun mount T5.

The mounting afforded a 27 ½-degree traverse either side of the centerline, with a range of elevation from -5 to +15 degrees.

While the pilot was equipped with a British Mark III 6 pounder, the U.S.-produced M1 was to be installed on production vehicles. A travel lock was provided on the hood, and the armored windshield cover, which was hinged at the bottom, was notched at the center top to clear the gun tube.

The gun shield as used on the T44 wheeled gun motor carriage was initially installed in the T48, but after initial testing this was replaced by a newly designed unit.

After testing, contract W-271-ORD-1023 was awarded for 962 vehicles, and Diamond T placed the T48 in production. The first 50 of the type were delivered in December 1942. These were followed by 174 in January 1943, 250 in February, 200 in March, 250 in April and 38 in May 1943. The vehicles were assigned Army registration numbers 4020934 through 4021614.

While originally intended for the British, actual deliveries differed. A letter from Brigadier Ernest Cecil Pepper, of the British Army Staff, Staff Duties Branch to Brigadier General John K. Christmas at the Tank-Automotive Center sheds some light on this. It reads:

"You asked me to present the situation regarding 57mm on half-track.

"912 S.P. anti-tank guns (T48, T49 or T70) were originally on the programme. The T49s and T70s were not produced in time to replace any of the T48s as had been intended, and, if no cancellations had been made, all would have been T48s.

"On 39 April 1943, British Army Staff cabled to the War Office that U.S. urgently required the half-tracks (T48) and would like as many as possible handed back.

"On 12 May 1943 the War Office cabled– "Prepared hand back all T48s to U.S.W.D." Thirty had already been consigned to India and despatched.

"A further 50 T48s appear to have been allotted to U.K., but there does not appear to be a requirement for them now."

At the bottom of this handwritten letter is a note, signed by Pepper, reading: "I gather that (illegible) has been accepted by Russia."

The 30 T48s mentioned above that were shipped to India were the only examples of the type actually delivered to the Commonwealth. The Soviets, however, were shipped 650 of the T48. Of the remaining 282 vehicles, the U.S. Army retained one in T48 configuration, and converted the other 281 units to M3A1 half-track personnel carriers at Chester Tank Depot in accordance with production order T-11453.

Above: *The armored windshield cover is in the raised position. It was fitted with two vision slots with sliding visors. The 75mm gun could be operated with the windshield up, although at the expense of the cover limiting the gun's minimum elevation and interfering with its traverse. (NARA)*

Below: *In an Aberdeen Proving Ground photo of 21 July 1941, parts of the 75mm gun breech and the rear of the gun shield are visible from the rear. Directly to the rear of the gun breech is the top of the pedestal mount for the machine gun. On the rear of the vehicle are a door, tail-light assemblies, trailer power receptacle and cover, and tow pintle. (NARA)*

Above: The interior arrangement of the 75mm Gun Motor Carriage T12 is revealed in this overhead photograph. Two fuel tanks were in the rear corners of the fighting compartment. To the front of each tank was an inward facing crew seat. There was a well in the floor to the rear of the support for the gun mount. (From the collections of The Henry Ford Museum)

Left: The 75mm Gun Motor Carriage T12 was armed with a 75mm Gun M1897A4 similar to the towed gun shown in this photograph. This cannon was designed on a French 75mm gun that the Americans had used in World War I. The 75mm Gun M1897A4 featured a Nordenfeld eccentric-screw breechblock; a bore of 101.77 inches; and a muzzle velocity of about 2,000 feet per second. With the APC M61 projectile, the gun could penetrate up to 2.8 inches of face-hardened steel armor or 2.5 inches of homogenous steel armor at 30 degrees obliquity at 500 yards. (NARA)

Above: *The rear body panels and rear door of the 75mm Gun Motor Carriage T12 have been removed to reveal the gun mount. Below the gun cradle, the cover is removed from an enclosure for the equilibrators, which can be seen arranged vertically. The equilibrators compensated for the forward-heavy mass of the gun, making it easier to elevate the piece. To the left of the equilibrators is the traversing hand wheel, and to the sides of the bottom of the cradle are the elevating hand wheels. Below the equilibrators is an ammunition bin. (NARA)*

Right: *In this photo of a 75mm Gun Motor Carriage T12 dated 5 August 1941, the cover is installed on the equilibrator housing below the breech of the cannon, and ammunition storage tubes with spring catches have been fitted on the ammo bin. Jutting from the right side of the breechblock is the breechblock-operating handle. (NARA)*

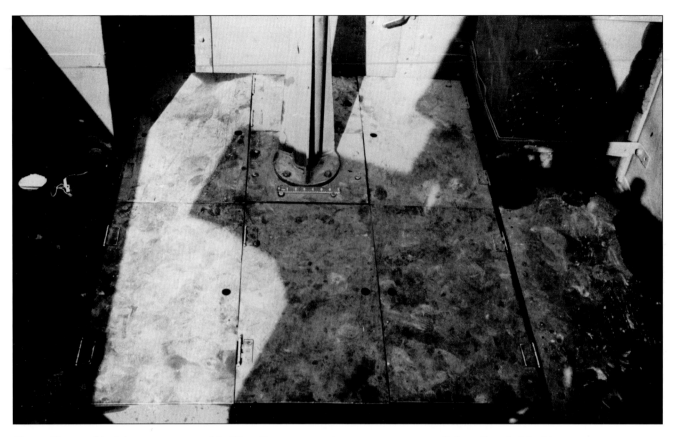

Above: *The rear of the fighting compartment of the 75mm Gun Motor Carriage T12 is shown, with the fuel tanks positioned to the rear corners. Between the tanks is the lower part of the machine-gun pedestal, with a 7-inch ruler lying next to the base for reference. Also seen are hinged floor plates, below which were* ammunition-storage compartments. **Below:** *Now, the lids of the ammunition-storage compartments in the rear of the 75mm Gun Motor Carriage T12 are open. Each lid/floor plate was attached with two leaf hinges. The photo was taken on 21 July 1941 at Aberdeen Proving Ground. (NARA, both)*

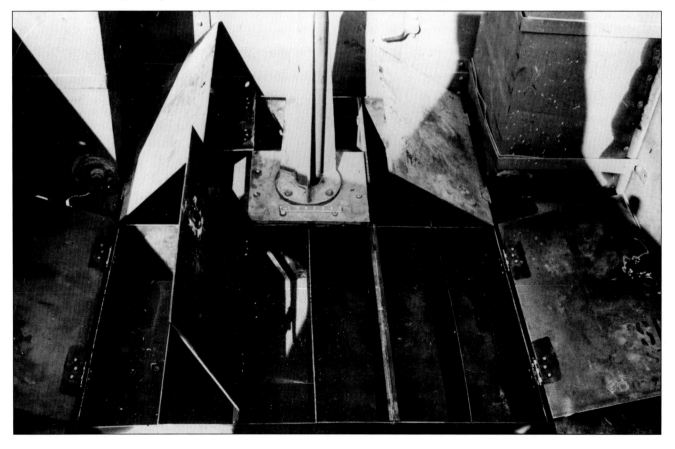

Above: *A 75mm Gun Motor Carriage T12 with the 75mm gun not mounted is the subject of this undated Autocar photo. The photo has the appearance of being intended for a technical manual or bulletin, with the background cropped out. Of interest is the heater mounted beneath the dashboard. (From the collections of The Henry Ford Museum)*

Below: *The Armored Force Board evaluated a 75mm Gun Motor Carriage T12 at Fort Knox, Kentucky, in the fall of 1941. In a photo dated 27 October of that year, crewmen are at their stations in the T12. A U.S. Army registration number, W-409580, had been assigned to the vehicle, and this is marked on the side of the hood. (Kevin Emdee collection)*

Above: *At Fort Knox on 27 October 1941, the 75mm Gun M1897A4 mounted on a 75mm GMC T12 is being fired at its maximum elevation of 29 degrees. The gun is at approximately full recoil. (Jim Gilmore collection)*

Left: *The 75mm Gun Motor Carriage T12 is seen from the upper right rear during testing by the Armored Force Board at Fort Knox. In the rear corners of the fighting compartment are the fuel tanks; note the filler caps on top of them. The tubes of the ammunition bin below the 75mm gun mount are visible. (Jim Gilmore collection)*

Right: *The 75mm Gun Motor Carriage T12 is viewed from the rear during trials at Fort Knox in October 1941. The rear door is open, affording a glimpse of the 75mm cannon and its mount. A gun sight is installed to the left of the cannon. A diamond-shaped symbol with the number 2 in it is on the left side of the body. Light-colored bars are painted on the bumperettes. (Jim Gilmore collection)*

Below: *An October 1941 photo at Fort Knox, Kentucky, depicts gun and vehicle accessories for the 75mm Gun Motor Carriage T12. Some of the items include aiming stakes (left); a chest and lamps (upper left); pioneer tools (upper right); a jack, rope, and two snatch blocks (right); and mechanic's tools. (Jim Gilmore collection)*

Above: *In December 1942 the Tank Destroyer Board subjected a 75mm Gun Motor Carriage T12, registration number W-409588, to tests at Camp Hood, Texas. In this 15 December photo, the vehicle has become mired in a mud slough that several other vehicles, including an M10 tank destroyer and light and medium tanks, had successfully negotiated. Tire chains are not installed; perhaps they would have helped the vehicle pass* *through the slough. Note the dust cover over the gun.* **Below:** *At Camp Hood in December 1942, the same 75mm GMC T12 is being put through its paces and has come to a stop while trying to surmount a three-foot vertical embankment. Although the vehicle had good cross-country capability, it was necessary for the drivers to take care not to try to negotiate obstacles and slopes beyond the half-track's abilities. (NARA, both)*

Above: *The original gun shield on the 75mm Gun Motor Carriage T12 provided little protection to the gun crew. To remedy this situation, the Army came up with several revised gun shields, including this rather bulky one installed on registration number W-409544, as documented in an October 1941 photograph. (NARA via Dana Bell)*

Below: *The same vehicle and revised gun shield shown in the preceding photograph is viewed from the left front. In addition to tall side and frontal plates, a small roof was included to offer some small protection from airburst shells. Note the opening for a gun sight in the front of the shield. (TACOM LCMC History Office)*

Above: *The Army also experimented with this gun shield, installed on 75mm Gun Motor Carriage T12 in late 1941. This shield had a lower silhouette than the previously shown revised shield. The tops of the side plates had a slight downward angle toward the rear. (NARA via Dana Bell)* **Below:** *The same* low-profile gun shield on 75mm Gun Motor Carriage T12 registration number W-409544 is viewed from the right side. The plates that constituted the shield were affixed to the body of the fighting compartment, with the gun firing through an opening in the front of the shield. (Patton Museum)*

Above: *A final gun shield tried on 75mm Gun Motor Carriage T12 registration number W-409544 is shown in this 29 November 1941 photograph at Aberdeen Proving Ground. This shield was attached to the gun cradle and traversed in unison with the gun. This design of shield would become the norm for the standardized 75mm Gun Motor Carriage M3 and M3A1.* **Below:** *After the production of the one pilot and 86 production 75mm*

Gun Motor Carriages T12, the vehicle was standardized as the 75mm Gun Motor Carriage M3 on 30 October 1941. Autocar manufactured the M3s, producing a total of 2,116 of them as well as the earlier 86 T12 vehicles. Production began in February 1942 and was completed in April 1943. Shown here in a 4 April 1942 photograph is the first 75mm GMC M3, serial number 87 / registration number 4017060. (NARA, both)

The gun shield of the 75mm Gun Motor Carriage M3 had two braces on the front. There also were two similar braces on the rear of the shield. A vertical slot was provided on the left side of the shield for the gun sight. (NARA)

Right: *The 75mm Gun M1897A4 in the 75mm Gun Motor Carriage M3 was mounted on the 75mm Gun Mount M3, as seen in this photograph. This gun mount was based on the Gun Carriage M2A3 and included a cradle, equilibrating mechanism, elevating and traversing gears and mechanisms, an elevating hand wheel on each side, and a traversing hand wheel on the left side. (NARA)*

Below: *This is a view through the assistant driver's door (or right door) of a 75mm Gun Motor Carriage M3 facing the front of the 75mm Gun Mount M3. The photo was taken at Aberdeen Proving Ground on 22 January 1943. At the center are the traversing rack and pinion. The tubular structure running laterally below the traversing rack and pinion is the carriage support. The A-shaped device at the center is the cradle lock. To the right is the right side of the windshield frame. (NARA via Dana Bell)*

Above: *When supplies of the Gun Carriage M2A3 dwindled, the Army began using a modified 75mm Field Gun Carriage M2A2 in its half-tracks. The modified gun mount was designated the 75mm Gun Mount M5, and the half-track that carried it was designated the 75mm Gun Motor Carriage M3A1. The front of a 75mm Gun Mount M5 is seen through the right door of a 75mm GMC M3A1 at Aberdeen Proving Ground on 22 January 1943. (NARA via Dana Bell)*

Below: *The first 75mm Gun Motor Carriage M3, registration number W-4017060, was used at Aberdeen Proving Ground as a test bed for a proposed replacement for the 75mm Gun M1897A4, the 75mm Gun M3, the same type used in the Sherman medium tank. For this experiment, the weapon was redesignated the 75mm Gun T15 on a Mount T17, and the resulting vehicle was designated the 75mm Gun Motor Carriage T73. (NARA)*

Above: *A 75mm Gun T15 on a Mount T17 is seen from the rear in a 75mm Gun Motor Carriage T73 at Aberdeen Proving Ground in a photo dated 2 September 1943. From this angle, the T15 gun is easily distinguished from the M1897A4 gun by the square, rather than round, breech ring. (NARA)* **Below:** *Designed mainly for the use of the British and Commonwealth armed forces, the 57mm Gun Motor Carriage T48 mounted a 57mm antitank gun on a modified Half-Track Personnel Carrier M3 chassis. Work on the pilot T48, seen here in an August 1942 photograph, began at Aberdeen Proving Ground in or by May 1942. The pilot vehicle was armed with the British equivalent of a U.S. 57mm gun, the Ordnance Quick-Firing 6-pounder Gun Mk. III, with a shorter and thicker barrel than the U.S. 57mm gun. (Patton Museum)*

Above: The pilot for the 57mm Gun Motor Carriage T48 was U.S. Army registration number 4019249, shown here during testing at Aberdeen Proving Ground on 16 June 1942. The initial shield for the 6-pounder gun provided scant protection from the sides. Later, a shield with better coverage would be developed.
Below: The Ordnance Quick-Firing (or QF) 6-pounder Gun Mk. III of the pilot 57mm Gun Motor Carriage T48 is viewed from the right rear, also showing details of the rear of the gun shield. The gun was mounted on a pedestal with triangular braces around its base, and the shield was attached to the carriage body (sometimes called the saddle: the traversing, yoke-shaped mounting for the gun and its cradle), so the shield traversed in unison with the gun. (NARA, both)

Above: *By the time this photo of the pilot 57mm Gun Motor Carriage T48 was taken at Aberdeen Proving Ground on 3 August 1942, the gun had received a new and improved shield, with a roof that sloped downward to the front and with more protection to the sides. (Steve Zaloga collection)*

Below: *The barrel 6-pounder Gun Mk. III of the T48 pilot is secured in a travel lock mounted on the hood of the half-track. The barrel of the gun rests in a gap between two individual glass windshields with metal frames. (NARA)*

Above: *In this Aberdeen Proving Ground photo from 3 August 1942, the 6-pounder gun of the T48 is at its full elevation of 15 degrees. The gun had a traverse of 27.5 degrees to the left or right of the longitudinal centerline of the vehicle, and an elevation of +15 to -5 degrees. (NARA)*

Below: *The driver's door of the T48 is open, allowing a view of the interior, including rifle scabbards on both of the cab doors. The fit of the 6-pounder gun barrels between the two glass windshield panels is visible. (NARA)*

Above: *A good view of the redesigned gun shield on the 57mm Gun Motor Carriage T48 is available in this photo taken from atop the hood. A box-shaped extension on the shield contains the sight aperture. The sides of the shield were cut out to allow clearance with the sides of the fighting compartment. At the bottom are the two windshield panels, including their windshield wipers.* **Below:** *A breech cover is installed on the gun in this photo of the fighting compartment of the 57mm GMC T48. In addition to the three crew seats with cushions, there was a round seat for the gunner, attached to an arm mounted on the pedestal of the gun mount. At the bottom is the lid of the ammunition rack, with a fuel tank to each side of it. (NARA, both)*

Above: *The ammunition rack between the fuel tanks is viewed from the front. The box at the top of the rack held ready rounds of unpacked ammunition and a bottom-hinged door on the front of the box protected the rounds from dust and moisture until they were needed. The lower part of the rack held ammunition in packing tubes and did not have a door. Two rounds in packing tubes are partially pulled from the rack.* **Below:** *Here, the door of the ready rack in the rear of the fighting compartment of the 57mm GMC T48 is open, and an uncased round is partially pulled from the rack. The ready rack had a capacity of 20 rounds, and the lower rack held 40 rounds. The angle iron with the retainer chain seen on top of the ready rack in the preceding photo was one of two removable locks for keeping the packed tubes of ammunition in place in the lower rack.* (NARA, both)

The top of the armored windshield of the 57mm Gun Motor Carriage T48 was notched to allow clearance for the cradle of the 57mm gun when it was in the travel position. The "U.S.A." part of the registration number on this incomplete vehicle has been stenciled on the side of the hood, followed by a roughly painted number, 4019249. (US Army Ordnance Museum)

Chapter 3: Howitzer Motor Carriages

The T30 and T19 HMCs

T30 75mm Howitzer Motor Carriage

With conflicts escalating worldwide, and the shape of combat changing such that more fluid forces were desirable, there came the need in 1941 for rapidly deployable artillery—self-propelled weapons.

The T12 Gun Motor Carriage having been considered somewhat successful, in October 1941, at the request of the Armored Force Board and confirmed by the Chief of Staff, G4, a program was initiated to mount a 75mm field howitzer in an M3 Personnel Carrier, in an arrange similar to the T12.

On 6 January 1942 the Ordnance Committee laid down the military characteristics of this vehicle. The new vehicle was designated the 75mm Howitzer Motor Carriage T30 per OCM 17665. The next Ordnance Committee action on this vehicle was OCM 17809, which authorized the procurement of two pilot vehicles.

Autocar produced the two pilots, shipping one to Aberdeen Proving Ground for testing—as well as to develop and install a shield on the weapon. The other pilot was shipped to White Motor Company for use as a manufacturing pilot.

The armament chosen for the new vehicle was the M1A1 75mm howitzer with M1A2 recoil mechanism. Mounting of the howitzer was to be via the 75mm Field Howitzer Carriage M3A1, which allowed a 21-degree left and 23-degree right traverse, as well as a range of elevation from -7 to +50-degrees. In order to achieve maximum depression, the windshield of the halftrack had to be lowered, otherwise depression was limited to three degrees.

Although the original plans included patterning a shield after that of the Howitzer Carriage M3A1, this plan was changed following a 23 March 1942 request to reduce the vehicle silhouette by at least six inches.

This height reduction was achieved, but at the expense of deleting the elbow telescope. This immediately brought about a request to investigate reworking the shields to make possible the use of the M5 elbow telescope, which not surprisingly brought the height back up to equal that of the original configuration!

The shield was returned to the original height, extended 8 inches to the rear, and initially lowered to within ¼-inch of the side armor of the half-track. The ¼-inch clearance proved too small, and was subsequently increased to ¾-inch. An armored flap was also created to close the gap in the shield above the tube.

Extended firing tests at Aberdeen concluded with only a few minor changes to the vehicle being suggested, and with the vehicle being recommended for production as an expedient howitzer motor carriage.

The Army desired to issue 42 T30 vehicles to each Armored Division and retain 60 in reserve for maintenance requirements.

Subsequently, in December 1941 White Motor Company contract W-303-ORD-945 for M3 Personnel Carriers was amended to include

105mm Howitzer Motor Carriage T19 U.S. Army registration number W-403065 is viewed from the front left. Early-production T19s had the non-removable service headlights with the grille-type brush guards. Later-production vehicles employed removable headlights, which were detached and stored before firing the howitzer to prevent blast damage to the headlights. (Patton Museum)

production order T-3212 for 312 of the T30 Howitzer Motor Carriages. These vehicles were Ordnance serial numbers 4004 through 4303, plus 12 without serial numbers, and were assigned registration numbers 409582 through 409893.

White completed the first 50 of these vehicles in February 1942, 94 in March and 168 in April. However, production order T-19179 was issued directing that 108 of these be converted to M3A1 personnel carriers, and that work was done by White in August 1942.

Ironically, White contract W-303-ORD-1611 was amended to include an additional quantity of 188 T30 howitzer motor carriages on production order T-3967. This change order appears to have been issued in February 1942. The Summary Report of Tank and Combat Vehicle acceptances, corrected to April 1946, indicates that all 188 were accepted, and the Chief of Ordnances report "Recapitulation of Facility Expansions for Tracked and Wheeled Vehicles from 1940 to July 15 1945" indicates that White delivered all 188 in November 1942.

However, the May 1945 edition of the Ordnance Department, Armored, Tank and Combat Vehicles 1940-1945 lists the serial and registration numbers for only 80 of the vehicles on W-303-ORD-1611, production order T-3967. The serial numbers listed are 315 through 394, and the registration numbers 4042505 through 4042584.

White and Ordnance records indicate that 500 T30 vehicles were built, and that 108 were converted to M3A1 Personnel Carriers. The registration numbers shown in the Armored, Tank and Combat Vehicles 1940-1945 listings provide sufficient numbers for the 392 vehicles that remained T30.

In addition to the vehicles converted by White described above, contract W-11-022-ORD-3630, production order T-19179, called for the conversion of a single T30 to M3A1 Personnel Carrier configuration in 1945.

T19 105mm Howitzer Motor Carriage

The 105mm Howitzer Motor Carriage was actually conceived a month prior to the 75mm Howitzer Carriage that became the T30. However,

the September 1941 request for authorization to construct the 105mm HMC was denied. The next month, however, the Adjutant General approved the request and Ordnance Committee action OCM 17391 on 31 October initiated the development of the vehicle, which was designated 105mm Howitzer Motor Carriage T19.

Like so many of the pilots of half-track-based motor carriages, the pilot for the T19 was fabricated at Aberdeen Proving Ground, with the Arms and Ammunition Section creating the mount, which was then installed on the M3 Personnel Carrier by the Automotive Division.

The weapon selected was the M2A1 105mm howitzer, mounted via the 105mm Howitzer recoil mechanism M2 and 105mm Howitzer Carriage M2.

Trials of the T19 pilot were underway in November 1941, and test firing of the completed vehicle exceeded expectations, but rough terrain operation of the T19 resulted in a bent frame. Reinforcing the half-track frame and redesigning the howitzer mount so as to distribute its weight over a greater area addressed this.

Concurrently, efforts were made to design a shield that would offer the howitzer crew some degree of protection, while permitting sufficient movement of the weapon and maintaining as low of a silhouette as possible.

Ultimately, the armored windshield cover was hinged at the bottom, allowing the howitzer to depress to -5 degrees. The maximum elevation was +35 degrees, and traverse was 20 degrees to either side of the vehicle centerline.

After testing and minor modification, the design was approved for production. Contract W-324-ORD-6289, issued to Diamond T Motor Car Company for M3 Personnel Carriers, was modified with production order T-3191 calling for the manufacture of 324 of the T19 Howitzer Motor Carriages.

Accordingly, the pilot was shipped from Aberdeen to Diamond T Motor Car Company in Chicago for use as an assembly guide. The first production vehicle was shipped in January 1942. After proof firing at Erie Proving Ground the Armored

Top: *Encouraged by the fine performance of the 75mm Gun Motor Carriage M3, the Armored Force Board decided to test a 75mm Howitzer M1A1 on a Half-Track Personnel Carrier M3. Work began on the design in October 1941, and the Autocar Company produced two pilot vehicles, designated the 75mm Howitzer Motor Carriage T30. Shown here in a photo dated 22 January 1942 is one of the pilots, registration number 4018410. (Patton Museum)*

Middle: *A 75mm Howitzer Motor Carriage T30, registration 4018410, is seen from the right side. This howitzer was commonly known as the 75mm Pack Howitzer. For this vehicle, the howitzer was installed on the Mount T10. The angled cylinder next to the rear of the howitzer was one of two equilibrators; there was a similar one on the left side of the piece. (Patton Museum)*

Bottom: *As seen from above, the 75mm Howitzer M1A1 and its Mount T10 took up relatively little space in the fighting compartment of the 75mm Howitzer Motor Carriage T30. The howitzer and its cradle were on a mount supported by two steel beams bolted to a flat plate. These beams, called legs, and the plate they were bolted to absorbed the howitzer's recoil and provided a stable platform for it. (Patton Museum)*

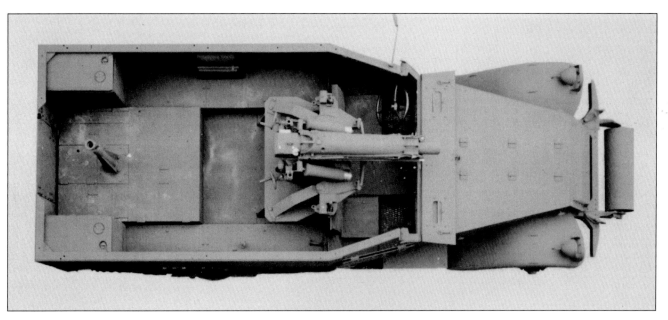

Force Board sent the T19 to Fort Knox for evaluation.

Diamond T completed 38 more of the vehicles in February, 136 in March and 149 in April, completing the 324 T19 motor carriages in accordance with the terms of the contract. According to the May 1945 edition of the Ordnance Department, Armored, Tank and Combat Vehicles 1940-1945, the ranges of serial and registration numbers assigned to these vehicles were 2 through 323 and 403377 through 402698 respectively.

Interestingly, Ordnance documents from 11 July 1942 provide considerable insight into the expedient nature of this procurement, reading as follows:

"1. This howitzer motor carriage was developed as an expedient item for the Armored Force to be replaced by the 105mm Howitzer Motor Carriage M7 as soon as it can be produced.

"2. The diversion of 324 Half Track Personnel Carriers M3 from the Armored Force, to be returned upon delivery of the 105mm Howitzer Motor Carriage M7, has been authorized.

"3. The diversion of 324-105mm Howitzers, recoil mechanisms and carriages, from the 600 whose manufacture has been authorized for use in the 105mm Howitzer Motor Carriage M7 has been authorized for use on the 324 Half Track vehicles, mentioned in paragraph 2. These howitzers will be removed from the 105mm Howitzer Motor Carriage T19 and returned to the American Locomotive Company for use on 105mm Howitzer Motor Carriage M7 as soon as the latter are ready for distribution to the Armored Force."

The U.S. Army fielded these vehicles from North Africa into southern France, the type finally being supplanted by the M7 Priest. Ultimately, the T19 was declared obsolete on 26 July 1945 by OCM 28557. Subsequently, Bowen and McLaughlin were issued contract W-24-200-ORD-812, production order T-18984 to convert 90 of the now-surplus T19 Howitzer Motor Carriages into M3A1 Personnel Carriers.

As with the T30 75mm Howitzer Motor Carriage, no T19 105mm Howitzer Motor Carriages are listed as being provided to the Allies in the 31 December 1946 War Department "Lend-Lease Shipments World War II," although that document excludes field transfers.

T38 105mm Howitzer Motor Carriage

The T38 was an effort to mount the short-tube low velocity T7 howitzer on the M3 Personnel Carrier. Study drawings were completed in January 1942, but no howitzers were available at that time. Accordingly, on the verbal authority of the Assistant Chief of Staff G-4, the project was suspended until the T7 was available.

By 25 May 1942 the T38 was listed as "indefinitely suspended," and indeed not even a pilot was produced.

An Ordnance Department history of this project states, "From all indications it was dropped due to the desire to expedite the development and manufacture of the 105mm Gun (sic) Motor Carriage T19."

Above: *The 75mm Howitzer M1A1 is seen again from above, this time with the 75mm Howitzer M1A1 at approximately maximum elevation. This piece had a range of elevation of +49.5 degrees to -9 degrees. Traverse of the howitzer was 22.5 degrees to the left or right of the longitudinal centerline of the vehicle. (Patton Museum)*

Below: *The armored windshield is lowered in this frontal view of 75mm Howitzer Motor Carriage T30 registration number 4018410. Both of the equilibrators are visible from this angle. Underneath the triangular travel lock below the howitzer cradle, the traversing sector is visible. Note the folded rear-view mirror above the steering wheel. (Patton Museum)*

Left: The rear of the 75mm Howitzer Motor Carriage T30 was typical of vehicles based on the Half-Track Personnel Carrier M3, with a rear door, channel-shaped bumperettes, mud flaps, an electrical receptacle and hinged cover for a trailer connection, and a grab handle and a taillight assembly to each side. (Patton Museum)

Below: The 75mm Howitzer MIAI and the Mount T10 are viewed from the right front in a photo dated 22 January 1942. The travel lock is engaged to the underside of the howitzer cradle. At the front end of the right equilibrator is a polished metal cylinder that fits inside the painted rear cylinder. A tompion or muzzle cover is fitted over the front end of the howitzer barrel. (Patton Museum)

Above: The cradle of the 75mm Howitzer M1A1 was significantly different in shape from the cradle of the towed version of the weapon, the 75mm Howitzer M1. For example, the M1A1's lower cradle, when viewed from the front, had a symmetrical "U" shape, while the M1's lower cradle was asymmetrical. The M1A1 had a lug on the bottom of the cradle for securing the travel lock; this was located below the two closely spaced ribs on the cradle. This feature was not present on the M1. **Below:** As seen from the rear, the elevating hand wheel for the 75mm Howitzer M1A1 was on the right side of the mount, and the traversing hand wheel was on the left side. On top of the breech is the vertically oriented grip of the operating handle for the breech. Below the breech and bolted to the bottom of the cradle is the elevating sector. (Patton Museum, both)

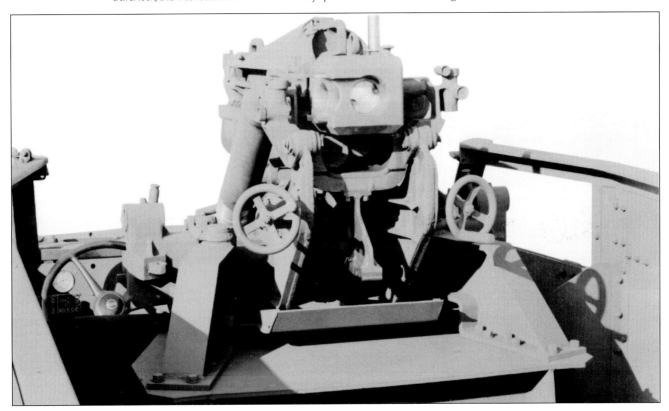

Above: The legs of the howitzer mount of the 75mm Howitzer Motor Carriage T30 were bolted to the top plate of a boxy, welded-steel support structure with a large opening on the rear facet. The elevating sector between the hand wheels is visible from a different angle; note the lightening holes in it. (Patton Museum)

Below: By the time this photo was taken on 24 February 1942, an armored shield had been added to the howitzer mount on 75mm Howitzer Motor Carriage T30 registration number 4018410. This resulted in an exceptionally high profile for the vehicle, particularly as seen from the front or the rear, considering the small size of the weapon. (Patton Museum)

Above: *The shield on the 75mm howitzer mount on the T30 is viewed from the right side with the howitzer elevated to approximately its maximum elevation of 49½ degrees. Note the rounded lower rear corner of the side panel of the shield. (Steve Zaloga collection)* **Below:** *The howitzer of 75mm Howitzer*

Motor Carriage T30 registration number 4018410 is at its minimum depression, -9 degrees, in this photo taken at Aberdeen Proving Ground on 24 February 1942. "T-30" has been scrawled in chalk on the side of the fighting compartment below the side of the howitzer shield. (Jim Gilmore collection)

Above: *An elevated view of 75mm Howitzer Motor Carriage T30 registration number 4018410 shows the flat panel at the top of the gun shield. This narrow strip of armor probably served more to strengthen the shield assembly than to provide the howitzer crew with any protection from airbursts or overhead fire.*

Below: *The shield of 75mm Howitzer Motor Carriage T30 registration number 4018410 is seen from the left rear. Note the brace from the howitzer carriage to the shield and the elongated slot in the shield for the sight. The thin gauge of the steel of the shield is readily apparent. (Steve Zaloga collection, both)*

Above: *Another 75mm Howitzer Motor Carriage T30, registration number 4018411, was photographed on 23 April 1942 with a revised shield. This shield was around six inches shorter in height than the previously shown one. This shield had the disadvantage of limiting the maximum elevation to 25 degrees, as shown here. (Patton Museum)* **Below:** *A 75mm Howitzer*

Motor Carriage T30 is seen from above with no shield mounted on the howitzer. A radio and radio antenna are to the right rear of the howitzer's breech, and a Browning .50-caliber M2 HB machine gun is on the pedestal mount in the rear of the fighting compartment. (Steve Zaloga collection)

Left: *At the bottom of each side of the shield of the 75mm Howitzer Motor Carriage T30 was a rectangular panel with two leaf hinges at the top. Although some sources state that these panels were raised to allow the shield to clear the sides of the fighting compartment when the howitzer was traversed, a study of the geometry of the shields and the half-tracks suggests that the panels actually were raised and secured to allow more head room for the driver and the section leader. (Steve Zaloga collection)*

Below: *Similar to the U.S. Army's requirement for half-track tank destroyers in 1941, at that time the Army also sought to equip itself with self-propelled artillery. As an expedient until it could procure fully-tracked self-propelled guns, the Army settled on the Carrier, Personnel, Half-Track M3 as the platform for a self-propelled 105mm Howitzer M2A1. Aberdeen Proving Ground produced a pilot vehicle, designated the 105mm Howitzer Motor Carriage T19, as shown in a photograph dated 29 November 1941. (Patton Museum)*

Above: *The 105mm Howitzer M2A1 of the T19 was installed on a Mount T2, converted from a Recoil Mechanism M2 and Carriage M2. The pilot T19 was assigned U.S. Army registration number W-409678, which, interestingly, was within the range of registration numbers assigned to the 75mm Howitzer Motor Carriage T30, suggesting that a T30, shorn of its howitzer, was diverted for conversion to the T19 pilot. The pilot 105mm Howitzer Motor Carriage T19 and early-production examples of the vehicle were not equipped with a howitzer shield. (Patton Museum)*

Right: *The pilot 105mm Howitzer Motor Carriage T19 is viewed from the rear. Above the body, the breech ring and breechblock are visible, to the left of which is the Telescope, Panoramic, M12A2. Below the rear door is the tow pintle, which is turned on its side. (Patton Museum)*

Left: *More of the howitzer breech and mount are visible from this angle. The howitzer cradle was installed on a traversing mount supported by two longitudinal beams with sloping rear ends. These beams, located below and to the sides of the howitzer, were referred to as legs, and they helped absorb recoil and distribute it to the chassis of the vehicle. (Patton Museum)*

Below: *In a left rear view of the pilot 105mm Howitzer Motor Carriage T19 at Aberdeen Proving Ground on 29 November 1941, the cylinder above the howitzer barrel is the recuperator assembly, which draws the barrel back into firing position after it has recoiled. Note the shiny metallic finish of the breechblock and the inner part of the breech ring. (Patton Museum)*

Above: *The pilot 105mm Howitzer Motor Carriage T19 W-409678 is seen with the top panels of the side doors folded down. Below the howitzer barrel is the cradle, which contains the recoil cylinder. The howitzer barrel is mounted on a sleigh, upon which the barrel slides back and forth upon the cradle when fired. (Patton Museum)*

Below: *A frontal view of the pilot 105mm Howitzer Motor Carriage T19 reveals details of the front of the recuperator cylinder, with two openings in its front. To each side of the howitzer barrel and sleigh is an elevating arc, with teeth on the fronts to engage elevating pinions. Braces for a howitzer shield are still attached to the mount. (Patton Museum)*

Left: *A 105mm Howitzer Motor Carriage T19 is parked at a factory with its howitzer elevated. The U.S. Army registration number, W-403065, pertained to a 1941 Carrier, Personnel, Half-Track M3, serial number 3187. The site likely was the Diamond T plant, where the T19s were assembled; just beyond this T19 is a Diamond T 12-ton 6x6 truck. (Patton Museum)*

Below: *The same T19, W-403065, is seen from a different angle. Visible on the side of the gun mount are the left sector, or elevating arc, with four lightening holes and, to the rear of it, the Mount, Telescope, M21, for holding the Telescope, Panoramic, M12A2. (NARA)*

Above: *The 105mm howitzer is set at approximately 0 degree elevation on T19 registration number 403065. The howitzer had a range of elevation of +35 degrees to -5 degrees. In this photo, the armored windshield has been raised. (Patton Museum)*
Below: *In the rear of the fighting compartment of the 105mm*

Howitzer Motor Carriage T19 were two fuel tanks and bench seats for the crew, with cushioned seat backs mounted on the fuel tanks. On the side of the howitzer cradle to the rear of the breech is the elevating hand wheel; farther forward is the traversing hand wheel. (NARA)

Left: *The fighting compartment of a T19 is viewed through the open rear door. The howitzer could be traversed 20 degrees to either side. The vehicle had little capacity to carry its own 105mm ammunition, with storage provisions for only eight rounds. For fire missions, the vehicle would receive additional rounds from an ammunition carrier. (Patton Museum)*

Below: *Crewmen stand or sit at their posts inside 105mm Howitzer Motor Carriage T19 registration number W-403065 during evaluations of the vehicle. Although six crewmen are present in this photo, the nominal crew of the T19 consisted of seven men: the driver; the chief of section in the right front of the vehicle; the gunner to the left of the howitzer; and four cannoneers in the fighting compartment. (Kevin Emdee collection)*

Above: *The same T19 and crew are viewed from a different angle. The crewmen are wearing M1917 helmets with tankers' winter hoods underneath. All are equipped with gas-mask bags slung under their left arms. Note the section of the howitzer barrel to the front of the elevating arc that was left unpainted, to allow it to pass smoothly through the yoke of the sleigh when the piece recoiled and was recuperated during firing.*

(Kevin Emdee collection) **Below:** *In consideration of the exposed situation of the crew of the 105mm Howitzer Motor Carriage T19 during combat, the Army experimented with various shields for the howitzer. This example featured an angled frontal shield that extended to the front of the cab, with triangular sides. The test-bed vehicle was T19 registration number W-409678. (Patton Museum)*

Left: *Another design of shield that was tested is shown here on the pilot T19 at Aberdeen Proving Ground on 27 November 1941. The shield is a stock one from a towed version of the 105mm Howitzer M2A1. Details of the rears of the howitzer breech and cradle as well as the supports for the howitzer are in view. (NARA)*

Below: *The shield from the towed 105mm Howitzer M2A1 when installed on the T19 proved to be flawed. As seen in this 27 November 1941 photo taken at Aberdeen Proving Ground, the shield jutted into the rear of the cab just enough to interfere with the driver. (NARA)*

Right: *This view of the pilot T19 taken on the same date as the preceding photo shows the extent to which the shield (top center) jutted into the cab. It protruded several inches to the front of the driver's seat. (NARA)*

Below: *A final design of shield for the T19 was settled on by the time this photo was taken on 23 March 1942. It had a cutout to the lower left to provide clearance for the driver. The hinged flaps at the top were shorter in height than those of the shield on the towed 105mm howitzer. (NARA)*

Left: *In a 28 May 1942 Aberdeen Proving Ground photo from the rear of the fighting compartment of a T19, the rear of the production howitzer shield is visible. A canvas cover is placed over the breech of the howitzer. A seven-inch ruler is lying on the cover for scale reference. (NARA)*

Below: *The same T19, registration number W-409678, is viewed from the left side with the dust cover on the breech of the 105mm howitzer. On the side of the elevating arc is an oval plate with the howitzer mount's serial number (not legible) and the maker's name, Pullman-Standard. (NARA)*

A W 409 678   T19

Above: *A 29 May 1942 Aberdeen Proving Ground photo shows the new, removable blackout headlight assemblies, installed on new brackets, along with the redesigned brush guards. Also in view are the movable armored slats to the front of the radiator. (NARA)*

Below: *The right removable headlight on a T19 is shown close-up with a seven-inch ruler lying below it. On top of the blackout headlight is a blackout marker lamp. (NARA)*

Chapter 4:
Multiple Gun Motor Carriages

M13, M14, M15, M16, M17 and Others

As was seen in the preceding chapters, the G-102 half-track chassis formed the basis for a number of vehicles. None, however, were as abundant or diverse as the Multiple Gun Motor Carriages (MGMC) that are the focus of this chapter. In addition to the G-102 vehicles, the International Harvester-produced G-147 vehicles also found use as MGMC.

No sooner than aircraft began to be used for military purposes, armies began working on ways to knock them down. The increased use of mechanized forces presented new challenges, both in terms of protecting a rapidly moving army as well as firing from positions substantially less rigid than terra firma. Compounding this was the increasing speed of aircraft. Early U.S. Army efforts centered on using manually elevated and traversed weapons mounted on truck chassis.

This changed when on 24 October 1940, OCM 16202 directed the procurement of a twin .50-caliber power-operated aircraft-type turret and installation of this turret on a ½-ton 4x4 truck. Thus was created the T1 Multiple Gun Motor Carriage, the U.S. Army's first attempt to develop a power-controlled rotating and elevating antiaircraft mount on a vehicle. Assembled by the Bendix Aviation Corporation, the T1 consisted of a power turret mounted on the ½-ton Dodge VC-4. The turret, drawing from aviation turrets of the day, featured two Browning M2 machine guns. During testing at Aberdeen Proving Ground from 14 June through 4 August 1941, the original guns were replaced by Colt-produced M2HB Heavy Barrel guns. The turret was powered by a 20-volt motor-generator set and a 24-volt battery system. The tests found the mount satisfactory, but the ½-ton truck inadequate as a motor carriage. The suspension permitted so much movement that the weapon was often inaccurate, and the vehicle lacked the capacity to transport adequate ammunition. It was recommended that the mount be tested on a half-track chassis. Such an installation was approved by OCM item 16989 on 17 July 1941.

The M13

Accordingly, in late August 1941 the turret was mounted onto a M2 half-track car, and the resultant vehicle designated the T1E1. While the installation of the turret on the half-track chassis presumably would provide a more stable firing platform, an Aberdeen report on the program noted these tests "...uncovered numerous deficiencies in this turret mount and resulted in action to procure additional power-operated turrets of the same general type but of simpler and more rugged construction with better operating characteristics."

As fate would have it, in November 1941 the W.L. Maxson Corporation presented to Ordnance a scale model of a proposed twin .50-caliber power turret. The design looked promising, and on 27 November authorization was given to Maxson to build a pilot turret, which would then be installed on a M2 half-track chassis, the resultant vehicle to be designated Multiple Gun Motor Carriage T1E2.

An M13 observed from above. The gunner's seat had a long notch in the center front to provide clearance for the gunner's control column. In each rear corner of the fighting compartment are two .50-caliber ammunition chests, stored at right angles to each other. (ATHS)

The Ordnance Committee also directed that the mount be tested on the new ¾-ton 4x4 Dodge chassis, stating that "it is considered advisable to defer the selection of the vehicle on which (the mounts) will be finally applied until further tests of the mount on the ¾-ton 4 x 4 truck, and possibly other vehicles, have been made."

The Maxson turret featured two .50-caliber machine capable of 360-degree traverse at a rate of 74-degrees per second. The mount had a range of elevation of -11.5-degrees to 90-degrees at a rate of 72-degrees per second. The gunner sat between the two guns, and behind him was a gasoline-powered generator that provided the electricity to power the mount's electric motor. That motor in turn drives the turret through a V-belt drive.

The Ordnance Committee, through action 17848, recommended standardizing the Maxson mount as the Twin Caliber .50 Machine Gun Mount M33 on 26 February 1942. This recommendation was subsequently approved by OCM 17928 on 12 March 1942.

While the initial authorization for the procurement of the pilot Maxson mount had indicated that this pilot mount was to be installed on an M2 half-track chassis, this was not the only vehicle upon which the mount was tested. Further tests were conducted, with the pilot M33 being mounted first on one of the pilots of the ¾-ton Dodge 4x4, and later on the 1½-ton Dodge 6x6 chassis. During the spring 1942 tests of the ¾-ton chassis with M33 installed excessive dispersion of the fired rounds were observed, which was attributed to the comparatively modest size and weight of the vehicle. Concurrent testing using the M2 half-track chassis, however, were much more favorable. While the tests of the 1½-ton chassis, which began in January 1943, were favorable, by that time the die had been cast for mounting the weapons on a half-track chassis.

However, the chassis selected was not that of the M2 as had been used in the initial tests. Rather, the test report recommended that "The Half Track, M3 would be a more suitable mount... for tactical uses requiring that adequate stowage space be provided in the vehicle."

This recommendation was put into action through OCM item 18062 on 7 April 1942, which established the military characteristics of such an M3-M33 combination. Designated the Multiple Gun Motor Carriage T1E4, the specification included provision for 5,000 rounds of .50-caliber ammunition. The Services of Supply approved these recommendations and characteristics in September of 1942.

Technicians at Aberdeen assembled a pilot in early April 1942, and after initial tests the vehicle was ordered into production. On 27 July 1942 OCM 18627 recommended standardization of the T1E4 as the Multiple Gun Motor Carriage M13. This recommendation was subsequently approved by OCM 19430. On 20 August yet another Ordnance Committee item, 18681, changed the military characteristics of the vehicle to provide for a front-mounted self-recovery winch.

Also in July 1942, contract W-303-ORD-1860, production order number T-4031 was issued to White Motor Company for the manufacture of the new vehicle type. While various sources indicate that the first vehicle off the White assembly line arrived at Aberdeen Proving Ground in December 1942, this contradicts other sources. The Summary Report, Tank-Automotive Acceptances indicates that 1,103 M13 MGMC were delivered, all in 1943.

The Recapitulation of Facility Expansion report details the delivery of the 1,103 vehicles as beginning with 85 vehicles in January 1943, followed by 270 in February, 195 in March, 320 in April and the final 233 in May.

Registration numbers for only 535 of the vehicles are listed in the Summary Report, Armored, Tank and Combat Vehicles listing of May 1945. They are listed as serial numbers 1 through 535, bearing registration numbers 4048234 through 4048768.

Field Service Modification Work Order (MWO) G102-W42 was issued on 29 October 1943, pertaining to the M13. This modification provided for a strengthened mounting for the M33.

Above: *The half-track proved well suited as a platform for light antiaircraft gun mounts. This Aberdeen Proving Ground photo dated 25 June 1943 depicts three types, from left to right: the Multiple Gun Motor Carriage M16, with a quad .50-caliber machine gun turret; the Multiple Gun Motor Carriage M14, with a twin .50-caliber machine gun turret; and the Half-Track Multiple Gun Motor Carriage M15, with twin .50-caliber machine guns and a 37mm automatic gun. (Patton Museum)*

Below: *The German Blitzkrieg of 1940 proved the power of air forces to disrupt and destroy concentrations and columns of troops and vehicles. The U.S. Army began thinking in terms of mobile antiaircraft gun carriages to combat low-flying enemy aircraft. To that end, the Army experimented in 1941 with this Dodge ½-ton 4x4 truck with a Bendix powered turret with twin .50-caliber machine guns, designating it the Multiple Gun Motor Carriage T1. (Patton Museum)*

The reason for the apparent discrepancy between the quantities, 1,103 vs 535, was the decision to convert 568 of the completed M13 to M16 configuration prior to shipment.

The M14

While it was anticipated that the White-produced vehicle was satisfy the need by U.S. forces, a similar vehicle was needed by the Allies as well.

On 28 August 1942, International Harvester representatives went to Cleveland to examine the T1E4, and determine what needed to be done in order to construct a similar vehicle on an International Harvester chassis.

On 14 September the Chicago Ordnance District asked International for a proposal to construct 12,711 such vehicles. The International-produced variant was designed the Multiple Gun Motor Carriage M14 by OCM 18964 on 1 October 1942. The Company responded to the request for proposal, and on 6 October the Chicago Ordnance District issued a letter production order for 12,711 M14 vehicles, all to be equipped with front-mounted winches.

The company executed this order, which became contract W-271-ORD-2502, production order T-4402, on 12 October. While Ordnance had hoped that deliveries could begin in November, International was not optimistic owing to the scarcity of materials. Owing to the intended use of these vehicles as Defense Aid items, in December 1943 the M14 was reclassified as Substitute Standard by OCM 19430.

In January 1943 the order for 12,711 vehicles was reduced 11,909 vehicles; the 802 vehicles that were removed that were to be completed instead as mortar carriers. Contract supplement number one formalized this change. On 2 March 1943 an even more drastic cut was made, with the quantity being reduced to a total of 2,800 M14 vehicles, with 1,600 to be delivered in 1943 and 1,200 in 1944. The mortar carriers were deleted entirely. An indication of the frantic pace and chaos of wartime manufacturing can be gleaned from the 9 April formal termination from the Chicago Ordnance District, which reduced the order to 2,805—five more vehicles than the previous instructions!

A considerable amount of further correspondence and changes ensued, with ultimately on 29 September an amendment being issued which called for 1,605 vehicles to be built as M14 and 1,000 as the newer M17. International accepted this change on 6 October 1943.

Even the actual production of the M14 was not smooth. The M33 mounts for these vehicles were considered free issue items supplied by the government. International's Springfield Works, which was building their half-tracks, received 289 of the M33 mounts in damaged condition. Owing to the urgency of delivering the M14, International was directed to repair the mounts themselves, rather than having Maxson do the repairs. The cost of repairing these mounts was $17,270.94.

Deliveries of the M14 began in December 1942 with five vehicles, followed by 20 in January 1943, 215 in February, 44 in March, 140 in April, 165 in May, 140 each in June and July, 150 each in August and September, 157 in October, 251 in November and the final 28 in December 1943.

Testing at Aberdeen from February to May 1943 reported that the M14 was comparable to the M13, and in fact was "exceptionally stable"—more so than the M13 in this aspect.

Of the 1,605 M14 Multiple Gun Motor Carriages produced, 1,600 of them were transferred to the British Empire through Lend-Lease. Reportedly most if not all of them were converted to personnel carriers upon delivery to Great Britain. Interestingly, Great Britain also received 10 of the White M13 Multiple Gun Motor Carriages.

When the concept of a multiple gun motor carriage was first broached, there was some discussion as to whether the armament should consist of the .50-caliber machine gun, or something larger.

The T10

The T1E4, standardized as the M13, was a considerable improvement over the previously tested

Above: *A G.I. demonstrates the gunner's position in the turret of the Multiple Gun Motor Carriage T1 in a photo taken at Aberdeen Proving Ground on 1941. The sight seems to be an adaptation of a periscopic sight that allowed the gunner to hold his head in a normal position when the guns were elevated. Although the T1 proved to be an unstable gun platform and did not enter series production, it laid the groundwork for half-track-based multiple gun carriages. (NARA via Dana Bell)*

Below: *A parallel project to the Multiple Gun Motor Carriage T1, the Multiple Gun Motor Carriage T1E1 featured a twin-.50-caliber Bendix powered turret on a Half-Track Car M2, registration number W-4011370, as seen in an Aberdeen Proving Ground photo dated 22 August 1941. This mount retained the periscope-type gun sight. Note the rolled-up canvas flap on the top of the support stand for the turret. (NARA)*

vehicles, most of which relied on manually trained weapons, but there was nevertheless a desire to increase the stopping power of the multiple gun motor carriage. One concept involved increasing the number of .50-caliber machine guns, while another contemplated larger caliber armament.

One of these efforts involved the mounting of twin 20mm Oerlikon automatic cannons on the Maxson turret. Maxson referred to the resultant mount, known to the military as the T17, as the Model 131. The M2 chassis, armed with the T17, was designated the 20mm Multiple Gun Motor Carriage T10.

Initial tests revealed that some modifications were in order. The Antiaircraft Command recommended that 110 of the improved mounts, designated T17E1, be procured. The May 1943 recommendation included a request that these be installed in modified M16 Multiple Gun Motor Carriage chassis. Four pilot mounts were built, and one was installed in the pilot M16, the resulting vehicle being designated T10E1.

The M33 twin mount had been redesigned to accommodate four .50 caliber machine guns, as described later in this chapter. The new mount was christened the M45 by the military, while Maxson identified it as the Model 116. The Model 116 was the basis for the Model 131. The conversion involved mounting new trunnions and trunnion segments in the trunnion frames. More robust, the new pieces were engineered to deal with the weight and recoil of the heavier Mark 4 Oerlikon cannons. Edgewater ring spring adapters secured the weapons. The trunnion segments featured weights to counterbalance the weight of the guns. The weapons could be fired electrically via Magnavox 12-volt solenoids, or through a manual pedal linkage. Both means trigger both guns. The guns are fed from 60-round drum magazines, and the magazines are specific to the right and left guns. The guns are charged hydraulically, using a manually actuated pump.

White Motor Company was issued contract W-33-019-ORD-578, production order T-10718 in October 1943 to produce these vehicles, and 110

were delivered in March 1944. However, none of the type would see combat. Aberdeen Proving Ground retained the initial production vehicle, registration number 40172310 for historical purposes through at least 1949. In November 1944 White converted the remaining 109 to M16 configuration prior to shipping, per contract W-33-019-ORD-2097, production order T-16577.

The M16 (T58)

Although the M33 mount was considered a success, the desire to increase firepower led to the development of the T61 Multiple .50-Caliber .50 Machine Gun Mount. In its initial configuration the T61 differed little from the M33, other than the addition of two more guns.

When the T61 arrived at Aberdeen, it was immediately installed on the same M2 chassis that had been the pilot for the M33-armed T1E2. Firing tests indicated that the dispersion was an acceptable and consistent 6 mils both laterally and vertically. Further, firing tests at the Antiaircraft Artillery Board, Camp Davis, NC, indicated that the four-gun installation gave a much higher percentage of hits on towed sleeves than did the two-gun mount. However, it was found that smoke from the guns could obscure the gunner's vision during certain wind conditions. Therefore it was suggested that the line of sight be moved from the initial position, approximately the center of the gun group, to a position 18 inches higher. It was believed that a periscopic sight so positioned would improve the gunner's vision and hence the ability to track and fire on targets.

Although the pilot T61 had been mounted on a M2 chassis, as with the M33 mount, it was felt that the longer M3 chassis would be a more appropriate motor carriage, and OCM item 18845 of 3 September 1942 designated such a vehicle as the T58.

Based on favorable tests and a recommendation from the Antiaircraft Command, the T61 with minor modifications was standardized as the Multiple Caliber .50 Machine Gun Mount M45, with a further recommendation that it replace the M33 in production "as soon as practicable."

Above: *The same T1E1, W-4011370, is viewed from the front with the twin machine guns trained to the front on 22 August 1941. The Bendix turret on the T1E1 proved to be faulty and, in the words of a U.S. Army report, "completely unsatisfactory," and was sent back to Bendix for repairs, and the Army did not pursue further development of this vehicle. (NARA)*

Below: *Another experimental machine-gun platform was the Multiple Gun Motor Carriage T60E1, registration number W-401964, which mounted a Martin twin .50-caliber machine gun turret, of the type used in Martin B-26 bombers, for example. The photo was taken on 25 January 1944. (NARA)*

These recommendations, along with the recommendation that the M45 turret be installed in a half-track in lieu of the M33 mount found in the M13, were contained in OCM item 19264 of 3 December 1942, which also proposed the designation of M16 for the resultant vehicle. This recommendations were approved and the M45 and M16 Standardized by OCM 19430.

The T1E4 prototype was modified to become the M16 pilot by technicians at Aberdeen in early 1943. Beyond the obvious installation of the quad mount rather than the twin mount, the conversion involved the installation of a 6-inch tall adapter ring, needed to lift the lower barrels over the height of even the folded-down armored side flaps of the half-track. Details of the stowage were also worked out at Aberdeen, thereby allowing the vehicle to be used as a production guide.

The Armored Force Board, Fort Knox, Kentucky, evaluated the vehicle and recommended that it be adopted for immediate use, with minor changes. Those changes included strengthening the base of the mount and its attachment to the floor and including acoustic padding to the plates forming the sides of the gunner's seat in order to lessen reverberation.

In November 1943, Headquarters, Army Service Forces, requested a further change. This entailed adding a platform on the rear of the mount to support two cannoneers. Such a platform was designed and on 7 September 1944 Ordnance Committee action 25035 recommended that all M45 mounts installed in M16 MGMC be so modified, the modified mounts being designated M45D.

White Motor Company's contract W-303-ORD-1860, production order T-4031 was modified, with the quad .50-armed M16 replacing the M13 as the subject vehicle. This change in production occurred in May 1943, when 160 of the M16s followed 233 M13s off the Cleveland assembly line. Production of factory-new M16s by White continued through the rest of 1943, with 269 being delivered in June, 354 in July, 320 in August, 289 in September, 323 in October and 324 each in November and December. Total new production of the M16 for 1943 stood at 2,323 vehicles.

Production of new M16s continued into 1944 and until the end of half-track production, with White delivering 300 in January, 204 in February and 50 March, making all-time new M16 total 2,877 units. In addition to the change order impacting contract -1860, additional contract W-303-ORD-4672, production order T-6648 of March 1943 saw 802 M16s being built, 426 of them being included in the monthly totals given above for 1943 and 376 in 1944. The final contract for new-production M16s, issued in April 1943, was W-303-ORD-5334, production order T-7844, which saw 178 M16s built in 1944.

The contract -4672 M16s were assigned registration numbers 4061290 through 4062091 and carried serial numbers 2466 through 3267; and for contract -5334 the registration numbers were 40122706 through 40122883 and serial numbers 3268 through 3445.

However, as alluded to earlier in this chapter, these were not the only M16s built. Unissued M13s and T10E1 Multiple Gun Motor Carriages were converted to M16s. White performed the conversion of 109 of the 110 T10E1s built to M16 under contract W-33-019-ORD-2897, production order T-16577. The vehicles were converted in November of 1944, retained their assigned registration numbers of 40172311 through 40172419 and serial numbers 8011 through 8120.

White was also contracted to convert 568 M13 Multiple Gun Motor Carriages to M16 configuration. This work was done in August 1943, and was done as a supplement to contract -1860, production order T-4031. As such, the serial and registration numbers of these vehicles are included in the block with the 1,897 new-build vehicles on that contract. The registration numbers assigned to the contract -1860 vehicles were 4048769 through 4051233, serial numbers 1 through 2465.

The final group of M16s delivered were 60 vehicles that were converted from M13 Multiple Gun Motor Carriages by Diebold, Inc., of Cleveland

Above: *The Martin turret installation on the Multiple Gun Motor Carriage T60E1 is seen close-up. To the rear of the ammunition feeds was the gun sight. Below the machine guns are ammunition boxes and the gunner's seat. To the front of the ammo boxes is a curved armor plate. (NARA)*

Below: *In a photo of the front of the Martin turret on a Multiple Gun Motor Carriage T60E1, a curved armor plate is between the machine-gun barrels. Fastened to the front center of the armor plate is a travel lock. At the bottom center is the pinion that drives the turret traverse. Visible behind the armor plate is the pinion and elevating arc for the right machine gun. (NARA)*

during December 1944. Diebold, a safe and lock manufacturer, also produced and installed the armor plate used by White in half-track and scout car production, so were well-suited for this work. The work was performed under contract W-33-019-ORD-2982, production order T-17610. These vehicles, serial numbers 8121 through 8180, retained their M13 registration numbers.

The British Empire was transferred two M16s under Lend-Lease, while the Free French forces were supplied with 70 examples.

The M17

Ordnance Committee items 19264 and 19430 on December 1942, which assigned the nomenclature M45 and M16 to the quad mount and quad-mount equipped G-102 vehicles, also assigned the designation Multiple Gun Motor Carriage M17 to the quad-fifty armed version of the M14. The M17 was classified as Substitute Standard.

On 19 July 1943, Ordnance advised International Harvester that of the 2,805 M14 vehicles on contract W-271-ORD-2502, only 1,605 would be built as M14s, with the remaining 1,200 vehicles being completed as M17s. A new production order, T-11082, was issued to reflect this. The company advised Ordnance that because the vehicles were so similar, there would be no cancellation or obsolescence charges associated with this change. This order was further changed on 29 September when 200 of the M17 vehicles were cut from the order, leaving only 1,000 of the type to be manufactured. International accepted this change on 6 October 1943. This change resulted in a charge of $962.00 to the government.

International delivered 400 of the M17s in December 1943, the same month it delivered the final 28 M14s. These were followed by 299 in January 1944, 300 in February and the final example was delivered in March, which also was the final month for International Harvester half-track production. The vehicles were assigned serial numbers 1 through 1000, and U.S. Army registration numbers 40175244 through 40176243. However, the

U.S. Army would field none of the M17s, all 1,000 instead going to the Soviet Union through Lend-Lease.

The M2 with Elco Thunderbolt

Arguably one of the most formidable multiple gun motor carriages was, like the T10E1, an adaptation of the naval 20mm Oerlikon autocannon. Built upon the M2 chassis serial number 1875 which had previously served as one of the four original T28 multiple gun motor carriage pilots (described later in this chapter), the vehicle was fitted with a Thunderbolt turret.

Developed by the Electric Launch Company, or as it is better known, Elco, the Thunderbolt was a power turret combining 20mm and .50-caliber armament. Elco, a subsidiary of the Electric Boat Company (since 1952 known as General Dynamics) had developed the system for installation on the PT boats for which it was famous, but limited numbers of the system had been installed on battleships *Maryland* and *Massachusetts* as well, and authorized for *Arkansas, Colorado, West Virginia* and *Washington*. Several variations of the turret were produced during the trial period.

The variant that was installed on the half-track was the Elco B-6, which featured four 20mm Oerlikon cannons in a staggered arrangement, which were flanked by a pair of .50-caliber machine guns.

With a rate of fire of 1,800 20mm rounds per minute, the Thunderbolt could lay down truly devastating firepower. However, the 560-pound turret and more significantly the recoil produced by the arsenal in the turret greatly exceeded the capacity of the half-track, and the project was abandoned.

The T28 Multiple Gun Motor Carriage

Prior to 9 March 1942, antiaircraft artillery was an arm of the Coast Artillery Corps. Consequently, it was the Chief of Coast Artillery, Joseph Andrew Green, who brought about the development of this vehicle. To comply with his request, four experimental multiple gun motor carriages were built in September 1941. OCM 17313 of 9 October 1941 assigned the designation T28 to these multiple gun motor carriages. Based on the chassis of the M2

Above: *Gun Motor Carriage T1E3 was another experimental project to mount a Martin dorsal aircraft turret. Army tests disclosed numerous deficiencies in the turret's drive mechanism, and the turret lacked the necessary durability for use on a ground vehicle. Hence, the project was discontinued. (TACOM LCMC History Office)*

Below: *The multiple-gun mount that finally proved to be suitable for use on half-tracks was the so-called Maxson turret, standardized as the Twin Caliber-.50 Machine Gun Mount M33. This mount, produced by the W. L. Maxson Corporation of New York City, relied on a variable-pulley power drive and was sufficiently robust to withstand cross-country automotive use. Moreover, it proved to be, in the words of an Army report, an "extremely accurate" weapon system. (Patton Museum)*

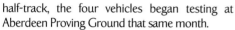

half-track, the four vehicles began testing at Aberdeen Proving Ground that same month.

The four vehicles differed in the way by which the armament, which consisted of the top portion of the 37mm Gun Carriage M3E1, mounting one 37mm gun M1A2 and a pair of M2 water-cooled .50-caliber machine guns. Serial numbers 1858 and 1874 both lacked rotating platforms for the guns, serial number 1875 included a rotating platform and serial number 1862 had both a rotating platform and a shield for the guns.

All four of these vehicles were tested at Aberdeen, and three of them subsequently tested by the Coast Artillery Board. The strongest criticism leveled after the Aberdeen test was that the vehicle lacked sufficient room for crew and stowage. Stability and dispersion was satisfactory, as was the tracking qualities of the weapon. Accordingly, Aberdeen recommended the use of the M3 chassis rather than the M2 for further development of this multiple gun motor carriage.

Counter to the results of the Aberdeen tests, the Coast Artillery Board felt that the T28 was relatively unstable and thus inaccurate. Further, the Board favored instead a vehicle with four .50-caliber machine guns. Accordingly, the T28 project was closed on 30 April 1942 per OCM 18152.

The T28E1 Multiple Gun Motor Carriage

The concept of a 37mm cannon-armed antiaircraft gun motor carriage was revived a couple of months later, however. In June 1942 the Services of Supply issued a memorandum that directed the manufacture of 80 improvised 37mm self-propelled mounts suitable for fire against ground and aerial targets, these vehicles being required for a special mission.

In response to this directive, OCM 18477 of 9 July 1942 authorized the manufacture of these vehicles, to be based on the M3 personnel carrier chassis, and designated the resultant vehicles the Multiple Gun Motor Carriage T28E1.

The Army turned to Autocar to manufacture these vehicles, with production beginning even

before formal contract W-670-ORD-2627, production order T-4081 was issued in August 1942. The contract amount was $547,000.00

The first 20 of the T28E1s were delivered in July, with the 60-vehicle balance being completed in August. To create the T28E1, the side and rear armor of the M3 was omitted, and the fuel tanks relocated to a position just behind the cab. The top carriage of the 37mm Gun Mount M3E1 was installed on a platform capable of 360-degree rotation. On the carriage were mounted a pair of .50-caliber water-cooled machine guns in addition to the M1A2 37mm automatic cannon.

The vehicle was stowed with 140 rounds of 37mm ammo and 3,400 rounds of .50-caliber ammunition, with 2,000 rounds of that being ready to use in ten M2 tombstone ammunition chests, and the balance stowed in a compartment at the rear of the vehicle.

In September 1942 all but two of the new vehicles were assigned to the 443rd Antiaircraft Artillery, Automatic Weapons Battalion, Self-propelled, which was organized in four 20-gun batteries. Because two of the T28E1s had been retained for testing purposes, D battery was also issued two towed 40mm Bofors. Once in the hands of the 443rd, a problem was discovered in that when the gun was at 15-degree elevation the ammo clip would eject against the frame, causing a jam. The 443rd modified the carriage to alleviate this problem, with the further benefit that the lower limit of depression was improved to minus five degrees, as opposed to the as-delivered zero degrees. Elevation remained limited to +80 degrees. The 443rd also installed radios in the vehicles, using civilian models owing to the shortage of military gear. The unit, with its T28E1s, was then ready for the "special mission" for which the vehicles had been created—the invasion of North Africa.

The T37 Multiple Gun Motor Carriage

As mentioned in the T28 portion of this text, the Coast Artillery Board rejected the T28, preferring instead that emphasis be placed on developing a

Above: *The Maxson turret initially was installed on Half-Track Car M2 registration number 4011370, as seen in this Aberdeen Proving Ground photo dated 24 February 1942. This was three months after Maxson delivered a model of the proposed turret to the Army. The vehicle was the same one that had been used for the Bendix-turret-equipped T1E1, and this package was designated the Multiple Gun Motor Carriage T1E2. Note the location of the single fuel tank to the front of the turret. (NARA)*

Below: *The Multiple Gun Motor Carriage T1E2, U.S. Army registration number W-4011370, is seen during evaluation at Aberdeen Proving Ground. In this photo, the .50-caliber machine guns are set at 0 degrees elevation. (NARA)*

multiple gun motor carriage armed with four .50-caliber machine guns instead. However, the efforts at this time (late 1941) were not toward the famed M16, but rather the T37.

The Ordnance Committee approved the development of this vehicle on 18 December 1941 via OCM 17548. United Shoe Machinery designed two different styles of mounts for four .50 caliber machine guns, and on 26 March 1942 OCM 17972 recommended that two pilots of each type be obtained.

One mount, the T60, had the guns arranged in two rows, with the lower guns positioned closer together than those on the upper row. The vehicle upon which this mount was installed was designated T37.

The second style of mount featured all four machine guns mounted in a single horizontal row, with the two outer guns positioned further forward than the inboard weapons. This mount was designated the T60E1, and the vehicle upon which it was installed the T37E1.

Both the T60 and T60E1 utilized the M2 aircraft machine gun, rather than the slightly larger and heavier M2HB (Heavy Barrel) weapon normally found on vehicles. Also, both the T60 and T60E1 were based on the upper portion of the M3E1 37mm gun carriage, as had been the T28.

Regardless of mount used, a three-man crew served the weapons, which were housed in a 1/2-inch thick armored shield, which traversed with the guns through 360-degrees. Elevation was through the range of +85 to -5 degrees.

While the impetus of this development was the desire to overcome the instability of the T28 that had been perceived by the Coastal Artillery Board and blamed on the recoil of that vehicle's 37mm automatic cannon, the Board was no more satisfied with the T37. Both the T37 and T37E1 were found to have functional deficiencies in both control and feed of the weapons. Accordingly, OCM item 19511 of 14 January 1943 closed the development project.

The M15 Multiple Gun Motor Carriage

While 78 of the 80 T28E1 MGMCs produced had been rushed to North Africa, this was far short of the 600 self-propelled antiaircraft vehicles that it was felt would ultimately be needed in that campaign.

Working toward the goal of fulfilling that need, the Coastal Artillery Board at Camp Davis, NC, conducted comparison tests between one of the original T28 pilots and the T54 40mm-armed Gun Motor Carriage. While the Board did not feel that either were effective as an anti-aircraft weapon, the T28, being further developed, was recommended for limited procurement, after some modifications.

The recommended changes included a repositioning of the lead setter's hand wheels, an additional lead setter's seat be installed, air-cooled machine guns be used rather than water-cooled, an armored gun shield be provided, maximum depression be increased, and provision be made for the collection of empty cartridge cases.

The Ordnance Committee approved the bulk of the recommended changes, but for an increase in depression from 0 to -5 degrees, owing to the delays in production this change would have entailed. It was recommended that the mount, modified as outlined above, was designated the M42, and the M3-based vehicle upon which it would be mounted was designated Multiple Gun Motor Carriage M15 by OCM 19087 on 29 October 1942. These recommendations, as well as the recommendation that the vehicle be classified as Substitute Standard, were approved by OCM 19198 in November 1942.

A further recommendation was made on 5 November 1942 when the T24 sighting system was standardized as the M6 for use on the M15, per OCM 19115. This was approved soon thereafter by OCM 19313.

Contract W-670-ORD-3216 was issued to Autocar for the manufacture of 600 M15s on production order T-4356. While Autocar and Ordnance records indicate that delivery of these vehicles began with 227 vehicles in February 1943, followed by 272 in March and 101 in April, photographic evidence shows that the production pilot, registration number 4083287, was at Aberdeen Proving Ground undergoing testing by mid-December 1942.

Above: *To compensate for the removal of the body to the rear of the cab on the Multiple Gun Motor Carriage T1E2, steel braces were installed from the cab to the floor of the fighting compartment. The ammunition chests seen on this gun mount would be the standard type used in the future on the M33 twin .50-caliber machine gun mount. (NARA)*

Below: *A man demonstrates the position of the gunner when the twin .50-caliber machine guns of the T1E2 were at maximum elevation. The guns had a range of elevation of +90 degrees to -10 degrees and a traverse of 360 degrees. At this stage of its development, the Maxson turret lacked the protective armor for the gunner that later would be installed. (Kevin Emdee collection)*

The vehicle, which tipped the scales at 21,000 pounds when fully loaded, had seating for a seven-man crew. Over one ton of the weight was taken up by ammunition, which was comprised of 240 rounds of 37mm ammunition and 3,400 rounds of .50-caliber ammunition.

As delivered, the production pilot had a moveable shield that moved with the guns. This feature was eliminated in production in order to improve visibility.

The contract amount for the M15 vehicles and concurrent spares was $3,724,000.00, and the registration and serial numbers assigned were 4083287 through 4083886 and 81 through 680 respectively.

Over 200 of these vehicles were issued to U.S. troops overseas, where their success spurred production of additional quantities of similar vehicles. In August 1943 the vehicle was reclassified from Substitute Standard to Limited Standard, and in July 1945 it was reclassified yet again as Obsolete by OCM 28708.

The M15A1 Combination Gun Motor Carriage

Owing to the success of the T28E1 and M15 in North Africa, the Army desired more M15 Multiple Gun Motor Carriages. However, the supply of M3E1 37mm gun carriages that were the basis for the M42 mount used on the M15 had been exhausted. Rather than manufacture more M3E1 carriages, the decision was made to instead use M3A1 gun carriages. Approximately 1,750 of the M3A1 carriages were available surplus, which would save time and money.

A report on the subject offered, "The 37-mm Gun Carriage M3A1 was an improved M3 type which mounted a 37-mm Gun M1A2, Sighting System M5, and Remote Control System M1 or M9. Acting on an implied request of the General Staff under date of 8 May 1943, a Multiple Gun Motor Carriage M15 was modified by removing Combination Gun Mount M42 and substituting the top carriage of 37-mm Gun Carriage M3A1, less the remote control, plus two Cal. .50 Machine Guns M2 HB and Sighting System M6."

Whereas the M15, as well as the other preceding vehicles in this chapter, had been designated a MULTIPLE Gun Motor Carriage, OCM 21226 of 5 August 1943 designated the vehicle utilizing the modified M3A1 carriage as COMBINATION Gun Motor Carriage M15E1. The modified was designated the Mount, Combination Gun Mount T87 by the same action.

After testing at Aberdeen in June 1943, the M15E1 was shipped to Camp Davis, NC for testing by the Antiaircraft Artillery Board. The Board reported that the vehicle, which was lighter than the M15, would be satisfactory provided certain modifications were made.

Among the requests from the Board was that a self-recovery winch be substituted for the unditching roller; that platforms be provided for the 37mm gun loader and the lead setter; that a rail be added to the rear of the mount to ease crew access; that the lead setters seat be raised so that he could sight from a seated position; that various interferences within the mount be eliminated; that the firing system for the machine guns be redesigned for a more positive action; and that the M7 computing sight be used.

Most of these requests were met, the exceptions being the inclusion of a winch and the use of the M7 sight. The vehicles were instead built with rollers and the M5 Sighting System. Thusly configured, OCM action 21281 of 22 July 1943 recommended Standardization of the T87 mount and M15E1 as the Combination Gun Mount M54 and Combination Gun Motor Carriage M15A1 respectively. These recommendations were subsequently approved by OCM 21563 issued on 11 September 1943, which also authorized procurement.

One reason that the M15A1 was lighter than the M15 was the reduction in ammo stowage, with the M15A1 being laden with only 200 37mm rounds and 1,200 .50-caliber rounds. This reduced the gross weight to 20,800 pounds.

Once again Autocar was contracted for the production of the vehicles. The company was issued contract W-670-ORD-4816, production order T-8050 in May 1943, calling for 3,000 of the M15A1. Deliveries of these vehicles began in October 1943 with 100 vehicles. These were followed in quick succession by 500 in November and 452 in December. M15A1 production continued in January

Above: *As seen in a February 1942 photo of the T1E2, the short chassis of the Half-Track Car M2 made for a rather crowded space around the turret, with consequentially less available space for accommodating crewmen and storing ammunition. For this reason, the M2 half-track would be discarded as the platform for the Maxson turret, and the longer M3 half-track would be chosen. (Jim Gilmore collection)*

Below: *A Maxson twin-.50-caliber machine gun turret is viewed from the rear. An unusual gun sight has been fitted between the machine guns. At the rear of the turret are elements of its power unit: two Exide 6-volt 152-amp batteries (lower left) with an electrical junction box with a voltmeter above it; and, to the right, a generator assembly, constituting an air-cooled, single-cylinder, 4-cycle gasoline engine and a Shunt 300-watt, 12-volt DC generator. (Patton Museum)*

1944 with 420 units, and the final 180 M15A1s were accepted in February 1944, bringing the production total to 1,652 vehicles. By that time, the U.S. Army had decided to abandon further procurement of half-tracks, and the contract was terminated. These vehicles were assigned registration numbers 40149399 through 40151050 and serial numbers 682 through 2333.

The M15A1 is notably distinguished from the M15 by the mounting of the weapons. On the M15, the .50-caliber machine guns are mounted slightly above the plane of the 37mm cannon, while on the M15A1 the machine guns are on a plane slightly below the cannon.

On 24 February 1944 OCM 22985 recommended the standardization of the M14 Computing Sight for use on the M15A1. This recommendation was then approved by OCM 23270. The M14 was a simple course and speed sight similar to the M7, which was used on the 40mm M2, and which the Antiaircraft Board had requested prior to production. Field Service Modification Work Order G102-W44 added guardrails to prevent the machine guns from firing into the driver's compartment.

Following the Standardization of the M19 Multiple Gun Motor Carriage, on 11 May 1944 the Ordnance Committee recommended that the M15A1 be reclassified as Substitute Standard. This was approved by OCM 24133. On 9 November recommendation OCM 25692 advocated that Combination Gun Motor Carriage M15A1 with Computing Sight M14 replace Multiple Gun Motor Carriage M15 in combat units at the earliest practicable date. This recommendation was soon approved by OCM 26128.

Although the M15A1 was reclassified as Limited Standard in August 1945 by OCM 28708, the vehicle continued to be fielded by the U.S. Army through the Korean War. While specific records have not yet been located, it is clear that 100 M15 or M15A1 motor carriages were supplied to the Soviet Union through Lend-Lease.

The T54, T54E1, T59 and T59E1 40mm Bofors

Once the U.S. Army began using the M1 40mm

Bofors gun in the field, its effectiveness against both aircraft and ground targets was immediately apparent. The M2 carriage upon which it was mounted, however, limited its mobility. Low-slung and a full trailer, the M2 and successor M2A1 carriages did not lend themselves to off-road operation nor rapidly bringing the weapon into action.

During a 25 June 1942 conference it was suggested that consideration be given to mounting the M1 on a half-track chassis. Despite its inclusion in this chapter, the initial effort in this regard was not a multiple gun motor carriage at all, but merely a Gun Motor Carriage T54, as designated by OCM 18508. That Ordnance Committee action, dated 16 July 1942, authorized the procurement of two pilots. Remarkably, Firestone Tire and Rubber Company was contracted to assemble the two pilots, utilizing chassis of M3 Personnel Carriers, sans the rear armor.

Completed in about two weeks time, the M1 gun was mounted to the rear of the half-track using the top carriage and mating base of the normal M2 40mm Antiaircraft Gun Carriage. In the new configuration the mounting was designated 40mm Gun Mount T5.

Using the standard direct fire sights, the only fire control equipment fitted to the T54, the gun motor carriage was tested at Aberdeen Proving Ground during July 1942. The Antiaircraft Artillery Board at Camp Davis, NC conducted additional tests. In both cases, the T54 was found lacking in stability, leading to inaccurate fire.

Ordnance Committee item 18698 of 27 August 1942 included some recommendations intended to remedy the stability problems. Chief among these were the installation of rapidly deployable outriggers, as well as reducing the height of the gun mount above the half-track chassis. Beyond those changes, the recommendation included the addition of armor protection and inclusion of a M5 sighting system. The nomenclature T54E1 was assigned to the improved vehicle.

The 27 August Ordnance item also recommended further 40mm Gun Motor Carriage pilots of other configurations. One of these was designated the

Above: *Because of space limitations on the Multiple Gun Motor Carriage T1E2, the longer M3 half-track proved a better platform for the Maxson turret. This combination of chassis and turret was designated the Multiple Gun Motor Carriage T1E4, and on 27 July 1942 the vehicle was standardized as the Multiple Gun Motor Carriage M13. When the similar M5 half-track was used as the platform for the Maxson twin-machine-gun turret, the vehicle was designated the Multiple Gun Motor Carriage M14. T1E4 registration number W-4019255 is shown during evaluation at Aberdeen Proving Ground on 8 July 1942. (NARA)*

Below: *The T1E4 featured an armored body around the fighting compartment, with hinged panels at the top that could be lowered to allow the machine guns to fire at their minimum elevation of -10 degrees. At the rear of the body were two storage boxes and a storage rack for four .50-caliber ammunition chests. (NARA)*

T59, which was similar to the T54E1 but for provision to connect the gun to a remote control gun director. That director was carried on yet another half-track designated the Half-Track Instrument Carrier T18. The second new pilot was designated the T60, and it is described in the next section.

Even with these improvements, the T59 proved to be unstable. It was suspected that one reason for the instability was the ever-increasing weight of the vehicle, which now hovered around 20,000 pounds. The circular armored gun shield was removed and the vehicle evaluated with various jacks, spades and outriggers. Ultimately, low rear and side-armored shields, approximately the height of standard M3 personnel carrier armor, were installed and the vehicle redesignated 40mm Gun Motor Carriage T59E1.

The T60 and T60E1

The second new pilot authorized on 27 July was the T60. The T60 was also markedly similar to the T54E1, differing primarily in that it featured a pair of coaxial .50-caliber M2HB machine guns flanking the Bofors, thus earning it the nomenclature Multiple Gun Motor Carriage, T60. The T60 went through the same variety of testing and modification as did the T59, including the installation of the low armor. This resulted in the redesignation as T60E1, which was accomplished by OCM 19274 on 3 December 1942, the same action that created the T59E1 designation.

Despite the considerable effort that had been put into the various 40mm-armed half-tracks, all fell short of meeting the Antiaircraft Artillery Board's objectives. This, plus the advances being made on the fully tracked T65 and T65E1 Twin 40mm Gun Motor Carriages—the T65 ultimately being standardized as the M19—led to the end of the 40mm-armed half-track projects.

The T68

As if the problems inherent with mounting a 40mm Bofors gun on the M3 half-track chassis were not enough, in February 1942 the American Ordnance Corporation proposed to mount two of the autocannons on the half-track chassis. Since the company's proposal included the provision that the pilot would be produced at no cost to the government (using government furnished guns and half-track chassis), in April the Ordnance Department accepted the offer.

Designated the T68 and delivered to Aberdeen Proving Ground in December 1942, the ungainly-looking vehicle featured the two guns installed in an over-under arrangement via a mount designated Twin 40mm Gun Mount T9. Probably due to the considerable weight, the vehicle lacked both armored cab and hood; literally it was built upon the M3 chassis.

Initial testing indicated that considerable further engineering would be required before the vehicle would even approach satisfactory, and in light of the encouraging study of the T65, the decision was made to terminate the T68 program on 24 June 1943.

Above: *When the folding panels at the top of the fighting compartment of the T1E4 were in the raised position, the twin .50-caliber machine guns were just an inch or so above the tops of those panels. Measuring sticks are leaning against the vehicle and are lying on the ground, for scale reference. (NARA)*

Below: *The top panels of the body have been lowered in this 8 July 1942 photo at Aberdeen Proving Ground, showing the enhanced clearance the machine guns would now enjoy, enabling them to fire at the minimum elevation of -10 degrees. (NARA)*

Left: *The rear of the T1E4 is documented, with measuring sticks along the right side and at the bottom for dimensional reference. From this angle, it is evident that the left storage box was of the same height but slightly narrower than the right box. Below the right box was a bucket holder. (NARA)*

Right: *In a view similar to the preceding one, the Maxson turret on the T1E4 is trained to the rear. Instead of, or perhaps in addition to, a regular gun sight, a large instrument, possibly a special sight, camera, or calibrating gear, is mounted on the gun sight bar. (NARA)*

Right: *A standardized Multiple Gun Motor Carriage M13 is viewed from the right rear with the folding armor panels lowered. Armor to protect the gunner now was installed on the turret, including a lower, bulged shield with two folding flat plates on top, leaving a gap between the plates for the gun sight. The stowage arrangements on the rear of the body differed from that of the T1E4, featuring, from left to right, a bucket holder, a small storage box, and a large storage box. (ATHS)*

Below: *In a rear view of a Multiple Gun Motor Carriage M13, details of the power equipment on the rear of the turret are visible. The gunner sat on a canvas seat, the front end of which is visible inside the turret. Above the seat are the gunner's controls, with twin handgrips on top of a box containing the firing-circuit switch and lights that indicated overheating of the guns. To the front of the turret are four stowed .50-caliber ammunition chests. (ATHS)*

The same M13 is viewed from above the front end. In the front of the fighting compartment, the locations of the fuel tanks and the four spare .50-caliber ammunition chests are visible. Each fuel tank had a capacity of 30 gallons; specified fuel was 72-octane gasoline. (ATHS)

Above: *The shape of the gunner's armored shell and the left-of-center positioning of the four spare .50-caliber ammunition chests are evident in this view. To the right of the chests is a metal tray. Note the metal frame along the upper edge of the fighting compartment, extending forward to the tops of the doors and windshield, and the hinged floor panels, with storage space below them for ammunition and equipment. (ATHS)*

Right: *The cab of an M13 is viewed through the right door, enabling a view of the underside of the metal frame around the top of the compartment. The seating arrangement was the same as in the M3 half-track, with the center seat higher than and slightly to the rear of the left and right seats. (ATHS)*

Left: *The M13 is observed from the rear with the armored flaps at the top of the body lowered. The Maxson turret is traversed to the rear. The gun sight was fitted to the H-shaped frame on the tube attached to the trunnions of the gun mount, to the front of the two folding plates of the shield. (ATHS)*

Right: *On the same M13, the canvas cover has been fitted over the Maxson turret. The cover was designed to fit over the two ammunition chests attached to the machine guns. (ATHS)*

Above: *With the cover removed from the turret of the M13, the twin .50-caliber machine guns are set at an elevated angle. The machine guns were Browning .50-caliber HB M2s, "HB" standing for heavy barrel. The turret was designated the Mount M33. (ATHS)*

Right: *From the front, the cover as installed on the Maxson twin-.50-caliber turret appeared much the same as it did from the rear. The ammunition chests that fed the machine guns delimited the shape of the cover as seen from front or rear. (ATHS)*

Further details of the Maxson turret cover are visible in this overhead shot. The .50-caliber gun barrels fit into canvas tubes sewn to the cover. Along the bottom of the cover were grommets with a cord passing through them, for securing the cover. (ATHS)

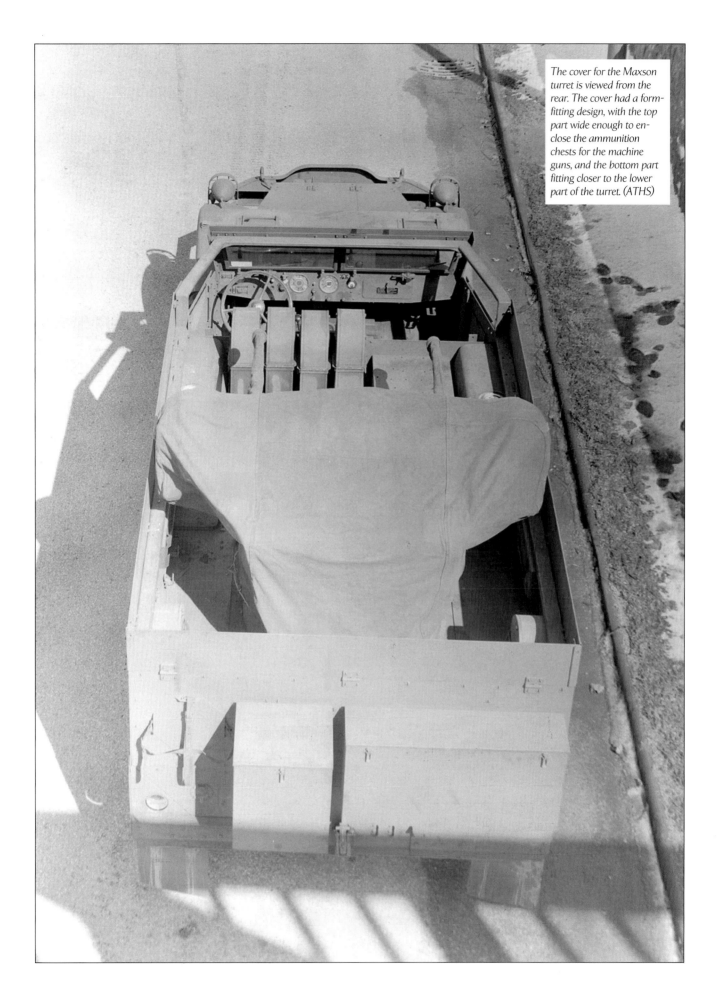

The cover for the Maxson turret is viewed from the rear. The cover had a form-fitting design, with the top part wide enough to enclose the ammunition chests for the machine guns, and the bottom part fitting closer to the lower part of the turret. (ATHS)

Above: *A Multiple Gun Motor Carriage M13, registration number 4019255, is undergoing tests at Aberdeen Proving Ground on 29 January 1943. The twin machine-gun mount lacks the armor and the ammunition chests, and the holder for a five-gallon liquid container is missing from the cowl.* **Below:** *In another view of the same M13, 4019255, with the armor missing from the turret, a clear view is available of the gunner's controls and hand grips, the gun sight, and the trunnions, the large, disc-shaped fixtures the machine guns are mounted on. Note the holders for the ammunition chests. (NARA, both)*

In addition to the Multiple Gun Motor Carriage M13, based on the M3 half-track, 1,605 examples of the Multiple Gun Motor Carriage M14 were produced, mounting the Maxson twin-.50-caliber turret on a modified International Harvester M5 personnel-carrier halftrack. A chassis destined for an M14 is shown here under construction. The folding plates at the top of the fighting compartment to provide clearance for the machine guns are installed. The side plates are folded, and note how the rear plate is set forward of the rear of the compartment, in typical M5 half-track personnel carrier fashion. (Clark County Historical Society)

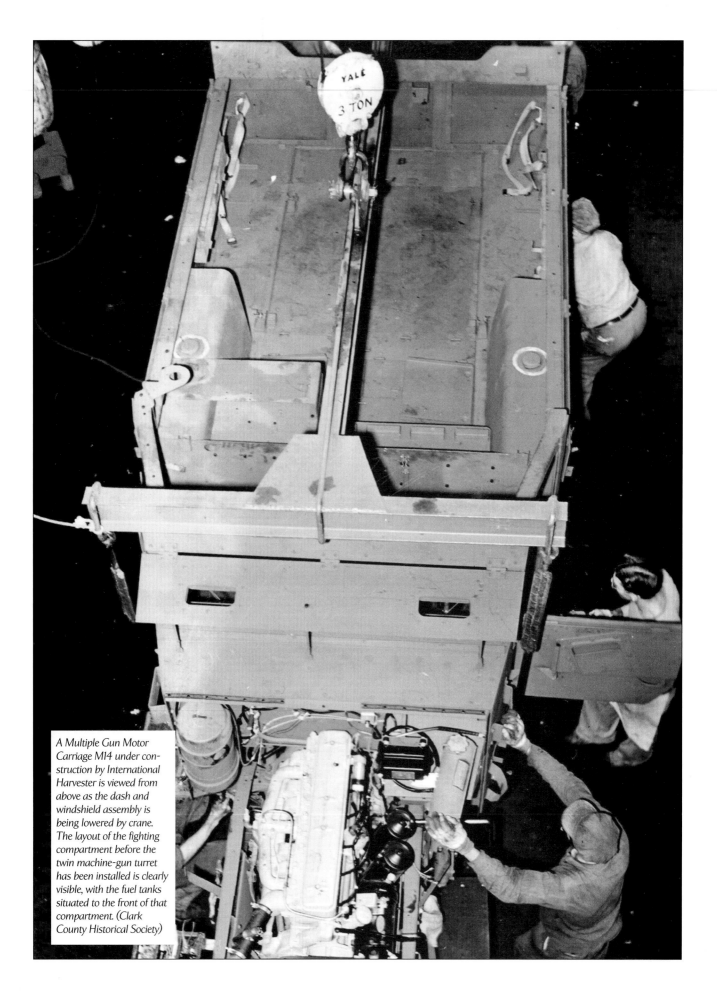

A Multiple Gun Motor Carriage M14 under construction by International Harvester is viewed from above as the dash and windshield assembly is being lowered by crane. The layout of the fighting compartment before the twin machine-gun turret has been installed is clearly visible, with the fuel tanks situated to the front of that compartment. (Clark County Historical Society)

Shown here is the fourth M14, registration number 4083890. (Patton Museum)

The folding side and rear armor of the Multiple Gun Motor Carriage M14 is visible in this view of the fourth Multiple Gun Motor Carriage M14, undergoing testing at Aberdeen Proving Ground on 25 February 1943. An ammunition chest is visible in the front of the fighting compartment, but no ammo chests are mounted on the twin machine guns. In addition, the gunner's protective armor is not mounted on the turret. (NARA)

Above: *The first Multiple Gun Motor Carriage M14, registration number 4083887, is seen from above. The fenders of the M14 were flatter in cross-section than those of the M13, lacked the M13's side skirts, and had a clipped front edge rather than a straight-across one. The folding plate at the rear of the body had a cutout on its upper edge. (Wisconsin Historical Society)*

Below: *To work around the curved rear corners of the body of the M14, the folding top plate on each side of the body terminated above the point where the side of the body began to curve to meet the rear plate of the body. This feature is visible in this photo. (Wisconsin Historical Society)*

RA PD 18532

An M14 is viewed from the rear with the Maxson turret removed. Like the M13, the M14 had a storage rack for four
.50-caliber ammunition chests in the left front of the fighting
compartment. Unlike the M13, the M14 had a single storage
box on the rear of the vehicle, with a single lid and three
compartments. (Wisconsin Historical Society)

RA PD 18533

Above: *The fenders of the M14 had a flatter cross-section than those of the M13 and also lacked the M13's vertical enclosures on their outboard sides. The ledge to the back of the folding plate at the rear of the body is a handy guide to differentiating the M14 from the M13. (Wisconsin Historical Society)* **Below:** *Further details of the shapes of the fenders of the Multiple Gun* *Motor Carriage M14 are visible on registration number 4083887. The front and side edges of the fenders were rolled in order to strengthen these assemblies. Note the unusual head-light brush guards, welded from steel rod stock; these were typical of the type installed on International Harvester half-tracks with removable headlights. (TACOM LCMC History Office)*

Above: *With the armor removed from the Maxson turret on this Multiple Gun Motor Carriage M14, details of the gunner's canvas seat and turret controls are visible. Note the individual retainers for four .50-caliber ammunition chests at the left front of the fighting compartment and the mounting bracket for a radio antenna above the right front corner of the fighting compartment. (Patton Museum)* **Below:** *A Multiple Gun Motor Carriage M14 without a U.S. Army registration number marked on it and with the Maxson turret not mounted is the subject of this Detroit Arsenal photograph dated 23 February 1943. Another distinguishing mark of the M14s, the curved steel bumperettes, is visible below the rear storage box. (TACOM LCMC History Office)*

Above: *The same Multiple Gun Motor Carriage M14 shown in the preceding photo is viewed from the front right, again with the machine-gun turret removed. Faintly visible in the fighting compartment to the rear of the cab are several M2 .50-caliber ammunition chests. (TACOM LCMC History Office)*

Below: *This M14, registration number 4083889, was the third M14 produced. The Maxson turret lacks its armor components. Handles are visible near the rears of the .50-caliber machine gun barrels, used when removing hot barrels prior to installing fresh barrels. (Patton Museum)*

Above: *As seen in a photo of an M14 with the turret armor removed, the gunner's seat was a piece of canvas stretched between a holder at the top and two rollers at the lower front. The gunner adjusted the seat by cranking the rollers, which tightened or loosened the seat. There was a gap between the rollers and a corresponding slot in the front of the seat to allow room for the gunner's control column. To the front of the turret was a footrest formed of a bent tube. Also visible are the elevating arcs below the machine guns and the cutout on the top of the rear folding plate of the fighting compartment. (Patton Museum)*

Right: *In an effort to bring greater antiaircraft firepower to its mobile forces, the Army experimented with a twin Oerlikon 20mm Automatic Gun Mk. IV turret on an M2 half-track in 1942. Shown here in a Quartermaster Department photo dated 10 October 1942 is what appears to have been the pilot turret, at this point designated the Maxson Twin 20mm Mount, Model 131. Apparently Model 131 was Maxson's designation for the mount. (Patton Museum)*

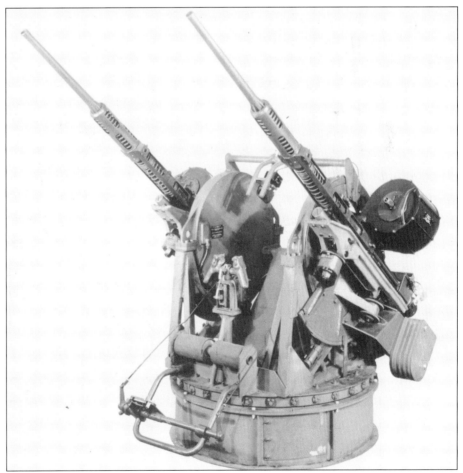

Above: *A new feature on the Maxson twin 20mm gun turret was two counter-weights on the trunnions below the rears of the 20mm guns. These offset the front-heavy weight of the 20mm guns, to allow smoother and faster elevation of the guns. (Patton Museum)*

Left: *The Maxson Twin 20mm Mount, Model 131, is seen from the front with the guns level. Sixty-round maga-zines are attached to the guns. Another new feature of this turret was the crossbar with a foot pedal attached to the stock footrest. (Patton Museum)*

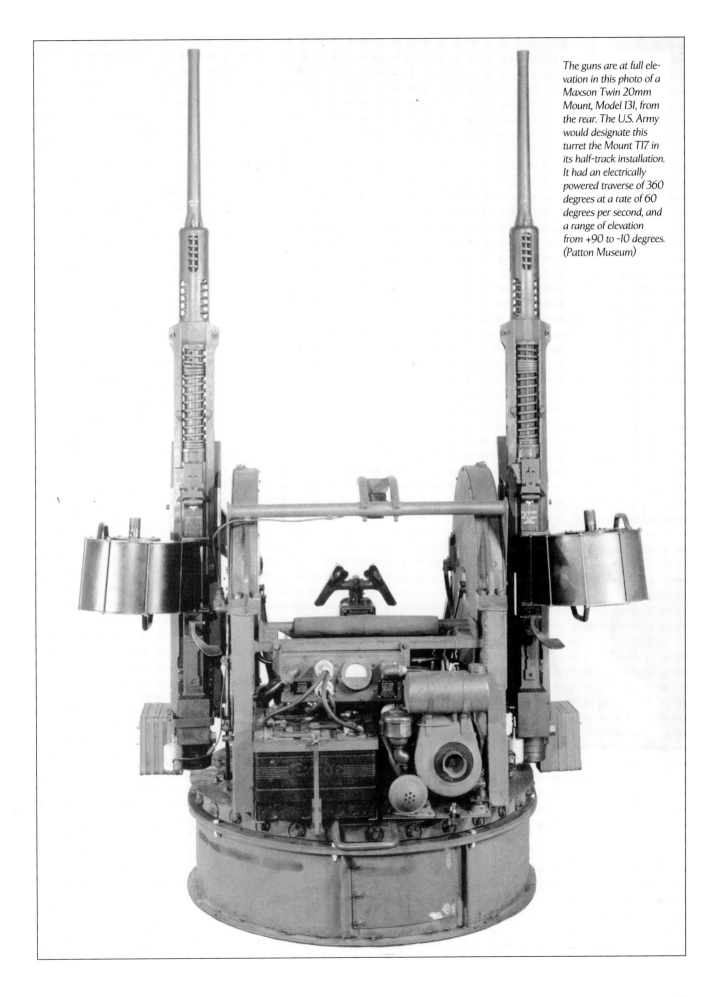

The guns are at full elevation in this photo of a Maxson Twin 20mm Mount, Model 131, from the rear. The U.S. Army would designate this turret the Mount T17 in its half-track installation. It had an electrically powered traverse of 360 degrees at a rate of 60 degrees per second, and a range of elevation from +90 to -10 degrees. (Patton Museum)

Above: *When twin Oerlikon 20mm Automatic Gun Mk. IV mounts were installed on an M2 half-track, the vehicle was designated the Twin 20mm Multiple Gun Motor Carriage T10. The Maxson turret in this application was designated the T17. The test bed was the same M2 half-track chassis used for the Multiple Gun Motor Carriage T1E2, U.S. Army registration number 4011370. The photo was taken at Aberdeen Proving Ground on 28 October 1942. (Patton Museum)*

Below: *The 20mm guns are at 0 degrees elevation in this view from the right rear of the Twin 20mm Multiple Gun Motor Carriage T10 at Aberdeen on 28 October 1942. The weapons had a rate of fire of up to 500 rounds per minute, with a maximum range of approximately 5,000 yards. They fired high-explosive shells that were capable of bringing down virtually any aircraft, and also were very effective against many ground targets. (Patton Museum)*

Above: *Visible at the lower rear of the right trunnion of the T17 mount on the Twin 20mm Multiple Gun Motor Carriage T10 is the counterweight. There was a similar one on the left side. The gun was mounted on two separate bearings jutting from the trunnion. (Patton Museum)*

Right: *The counterweights are seen from the rear on the T17 mount. Each counterweight consisted of 10 steel plates, bolted in a group to brackets mounted on the trunnions. Also visible are the batteries, electrical junction box, generator motor, and gasoline tank. (Patton Museum)*

154

Above: The guns of a Twin 20mm Multiple Gun Motor Carriage T10 are depressed and traversed to the left, and are undergoing charging, at Aberdeen Proving Ground on 28 October 1942. The two bolts that hold the counterbalance assembly to its bracket are apparent. (Patton Museum)

Below: The ammunition magazines are installed on the 20mm guns on a T10 at Aberdeen Proving Ground, 28 October 1942. The magazines had a capacity of 60 rounds and used a spring to feed ammunition to the guns. A grab handle was on the front and on the rear of each magazine. (Patton Museum)

Above: *A crew is manning the twin 20mm guns of a Multiple Gun Motor Carriage T10. The gunner is seated in the turret, and loaders are standing by in the positions they would be assuming were they preparing to replenish the 60-round magazines.*
Below: *The footrest of the Maxson turret of the Twin 20mm Multiple Gun Motor Carriage T10 incorporated a clamped-on crossbar with a foot pedal on the right side. This pedal had an electrical or a mechanical cable hooked to it and apparently was a control mechanism of some sort. The man seated in the turret has his hands on the control grips. Each grip had a trigger, and the gunner moved the grips to control the guns' elevation and azimuth. (Kevin Emdee collection, both)*

Above: *Following testing of the Twin 20mm Multiple Gun Motor Carriage T10 and the identification of corrective revisions, the Antiaircraft Command authorized procurement of 110 production vehicles, designated the Twin 20mm Multiple Gun Motor Carriage T10E1. These constituted a modified .50-caliber Multiple Gun Motor Carriage M16 chassis with T17E1 20mm gun mount. On the vehicle shown here, angle irons were attached to the main side plates of the fighting compartment at* the level of the bottom of the folding upper plates; these acted as stops to hold the folding plates horizontal when folded down.
Below: *On the rear of the 20mm Multiple Gun Motor Carriage T10E1 were two storage boxes, with the right one wider but slightly less tall than the left one. The face of a man sitting in the gunner's position in the turret is visible between the two hinged plates at the top of the shield. (ATHS, both)*

Above: *The gunner is training the twin guns of a 20mm Multiple Gun Motor Carriage T10E1 to the rear. Jutting at an angle from the center rear of the body is a holder for the folding rear plate when in the lowered position. (ATHS)*

Right: *The White Motor Company produced all 110 T10E1s in March 1944, but all but one were converted subsequently to Multiple Gun Motor Carriages M16. The gun sight specified for the T10E1 was the Reflex Sight Mk. 9. (ATHS)*

Above: *A clear view is provided of the Oerlikon 20mm Guns Mk. IV on a 20mm Multiple Gun Motor Carriage T10E1. The guns are trained to the right rear. In the rear corners of the fighting compartment are storage boxes with pentagonal lids. (ATHS)*

Left: *On the T10E1, the bulky steel counterweights of the 20mm gun mount of the T10 were replaced by more compact counterbalances on the outboard sides of the rears of the guns. These counterbalances apparently used spiral springs to offset the forward-heavy weight of the guns. (ATHS)*

Above: *In an Aberdeen Proving Ground photo dated 3 January 1944, the T17E1 20mm gun mount is seen from above. The counterbalances are visible to the rears of the outboard sides of the 20mm guns. Two seats and ammunition racks are to the front of the gun mount in the fighting compartment. (Patton Museum)*

Below: *"TWIN 20MM GMC T17E1" is scrawled on the left side of the vehicle undergoing testing at Aberdeen Proving Ground on 3 January 1944. A bucket is secured to the rear of the body with cross straps. Sixty-round ammunition magazines are clipped to the 20mm guns. A ruler is leaning against the left track. (Patton Museum)*

Above: *All but one of the 110 production T10E1s were converted to M16 multiple gun motor carriages. Seen here is the sole vehicle that was not converted: registration number 40172310, is parked at Aberdeen Proving Ground in a photo dated 21 February 1949. The twin 20mm guns had been dismounted. This vehicle, serial number 8011, was the first of the 110 production T10E1s; their registration numbers ran from 40172310 to 40172419, and their serial numbers were 8011 to 8120. (US Army Ordnance Museum)*

Left: *Desiring a more powerful multiple gun mount for its half-tracks than the Maxson Twin Caliber-.50 Machine Gun Mount M33, the Army ordered development of a four-gun ("quad") .50-caliber mount in April 1942. The resulting .50-caliber Machine Gun Mount T61 was based on the Maxson M33 turret but with provisions for two .50-caliber machine guns on each side. The turret is seen from the right side with the guns at an elevation of 0 degrees. (Patton Museum)*

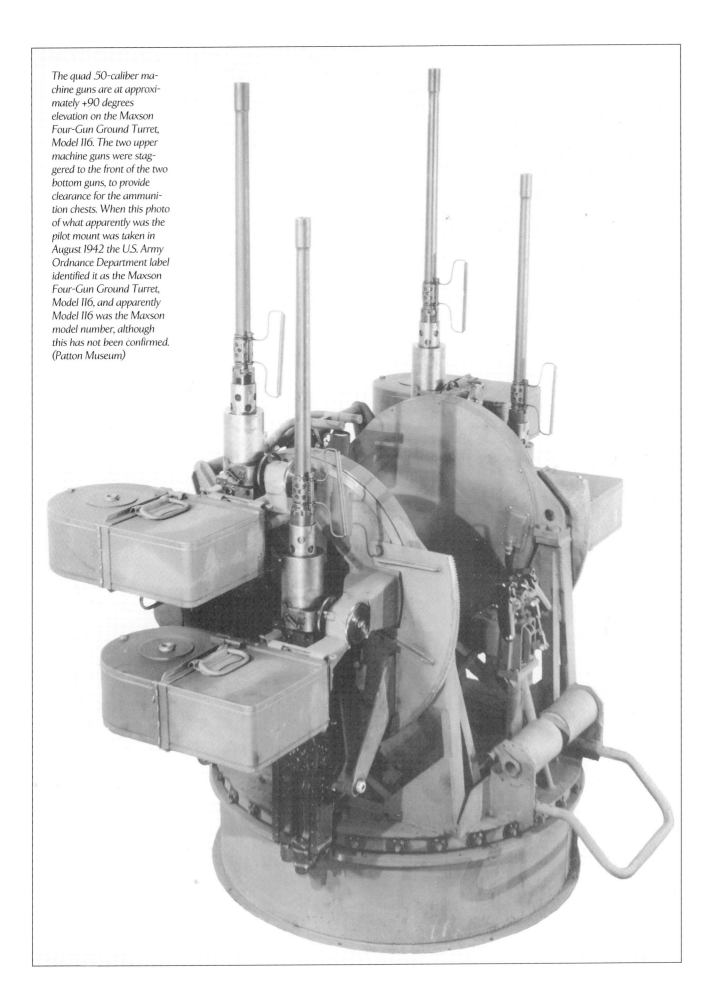

The quad .50-caliber machine guns are at approximately +90 degrees elevation on the Maxson Four-Gun Ground Turret, Model 116. The two upper machine guns were staggered to the front of the two bottom guns, to provide clearance for the ammunition chests. When this photo of what apparently was the pilot mount was taken in August 1942 the U.S. Army Ordnance Department label identified it as the Maxson Four-Gun Ground Turret, Model 116, and apparently Model 116 was the Maxson model number, although this has not been confirmed. (Patton Museum)

Left: *The machine guns are depressed to their minimum elevation, -10 degrees, on the Maxson Four-Gun Ground Turret, Model 116. With no armor shield installed, the gunner's footrest protruding from the front of the turret is visible. (Patton Museum)*

Below: *A man in civilian dress is seated in the Maxson Four-Gun Ground Turret, Model 116, providing a good idea of the positioning of the gunner in the turret. His hands are on the control grips, and he is peering through the gun sight. The grips were turned on a horizontal axis to traverse the turret: counterclockwise for left and clockwise for right. (Patton Museum)*

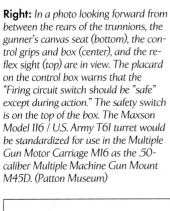

Right: *In a photo looking forward from between the rears of the trunnions, the gunner's canvas seat (bottom), the control grips and box (center), and the reflex sight (top) are in view. The placard on the control box warns that the "Firing circuit switch should be "safe" except during action." The safety switch is on the top of the box. The Maxson Model 116 / U.S. Army T61 turret would be standardized for use in the Multiple Gun Motor Carriage M16 as the .50-caliber Multiple Machine Gun Mount M45D. (Patton Museum)*

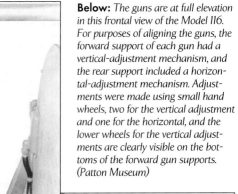

Below: *The guns are at full elevation in this frontal view of the Model 116. For purposes of aligning the guns, the forward support of each gun had a vertical-adjustment mechanism, and the rear support included a horizontal-adjustment mechanism. Adjustments were made using small hand wheels, two for the vertical adjustment and one for the horizontal, and the lower wheels for the vertical adjustments are clearly visible on the bottoms of the forward gun supports. (Patton Museum)*

Above: A towed version of the quad .50-caliber machine gun mount was produced, standardized as the .50-caliber Multiple Gun Carriage M55, consisting of a .50-Caliber Multiple Machine Gun Mount M45E1 on a trailer. The photographs of an example are provided here for details of the quad gun mount, similar to the M45D quad mount of the Multiple Gun Motor Carriage M16. **Below:** The .50-caliber Multiple Gun Carriage M55 is shown with the wheels installed on the trailer, hitched to a Jeep. On the trailer coupling was a long lever, angled to the rear, with a rope attached to it, for remotely uncoupling the gun mount in an emergency. (Patton Museum, both)

Right: *The M55 had three lift jacks, one at the front, as seen here, and two at the rear, for quickly raising the gun mount for removing the wheels. After the wheels were removed, the gun mount was lowered to the ground for firing. M2 ammunition chests are fitted to the mount. (Patton Museum)*

Below: *The two lift jacks at the rear of the M55 are shown in the raised position with the trailer wheels detached. The mount was equipped with either the Reflex Sight M18 or the Illuminated Sight Mk. 9 Mod. 1. The storage batteries have been removed from the left side of the generator in this photo. (Patton Museum)*

Above: *A minor feature worthy of notice on the M55 is the blade-shaped fitting on the turret floor, below the perforated barrel support to the front of the receiver of the lower machine gun. This blade acted as a stop to prevent the guns from depressing lower than -10 degrees. To accomplish this, the blade made contact with a stud on the lower front of the sector, or elevating arc. (Patton Museum)* **Below:** *A .50-Caliber Multiple*

Machine Gun Mount T61 was undergoing testing on an M2 half-track at Aberdeen Proving Ground by the time this photo was taken on 24 August 1942. The test vehicle was registration number W-4011370, the same one that had been used for two earlier, Maxson-turret-equipped multiple gun motor carriages, the T1E1 and T1E2. (NARA)

Above: *The .50-Caliber Multiple Machine Gun Mount T61 was standardized as the .50-Caliber Multiple Machine Gun Mount M45 in December 1942, and when the M45D version of this quad gun mount was used on the M3 half-track, the result was the Multiple Gun Motor Carriage M16. This 2 February 1943 Aberdeen Proving Ground photograph shows the pilot* M16, registration number W-4019255. **Below:** *The same M16 is seen from the left rear with the folding panels at the top of the fighting compartment lowered. The shield had not been installed on the gun mount, and the M2 ammunition chests were not installed on the mount either. (NARA, both)*

Left: *The pilot Multiple Gun Motor Carriage M16, registration number W-4019255, is viewed from the upper rear with the guns trained aft. The rear of the body featured, left to right, a bucket holder, a small storage box, and a large storage box, with channel-iron-type bumperettes and a tow pintle to the bottom. (NARA)*

Below: *On production M16s, the folding side panels on the fighting compartment had cutouts on their upper sides, to provide clearance for the lower (rear) ammunition chests. Note the stored ammunition chests to the rear of the driver's seat. (Patton Museum)*

Above: *An M16 is seen with the folding armored panels on the fighting compartment in the raised position. The lower, or rear, .50-caliber ammunition chests actually jutted slightly outside of the body when the turret was trained to the front or to the rear.* **Below:** *White Motor Company manufactured the Multiple Gun Motor Carriage M16 from May 1943 to March 1944. Ac-cording to the exhaustive list of contracts, serial numbers, and U.S. Army registration numbers in the 1 May 1945 edition of Ordnance Department Armored, Tank, and Combat Vehicles, 1940-1945, a total of 3,615 M16s were produced, including vehicles assembled by White and conversions of T10E1 and M13 half-track multiple gun motor carriages. (ATHS, both)*

Left: *The folding panel on the rear of the fighting compartment of the M16 also had a cutout to provide clearance for the lower .50-caliber ammunition chests. The turret armor was the same as that for the twin-gun Maxson turrets, with a lower shell and two hinged plates on top, with space between them for the gun sight. (ATHS)*

Below: *A Multiple Gun Motor Carriage M16 is seen from above. A standard rack for four .50-caliber ammunition chests is between the front ends of the fuel tanks, but on this vehicle there is an additional, nonstandard rack for two more ammo chests between the two seats in the cab. Duffel bags are piled on the floor to the front of the turret. (Patton Museum)*

Above: *U.S. Army officers are seated in the vehicle, a crowd of civilians stands to the sides, and a film crew is shooting footage to the far left during a firing demonstration of a Multiple Gun Motor Carriage M16. Note the spare headlights stored to the rear of the driver's door. (ATHS)*

Below: *As civilian photographers (right) document the occasion, the gunner in the same Multiple Gun Motor Carriage M16 shown in the preceding photo is preparing to fire the quad .50-caliber machine guns toward the body of water in the background. (ATHS)*

Left: *The same gunner pauses between firing bursts from the quad .50-caliber machine gun. Spent cartridges litter the floor to the sides and front of the turret. The small placard on the base of the turret is marked "center line / cab end" with a vertical reference line. (ATHS)*

Below: *Another view from the M16 gunnery demonstration shows the power equipment at the rear of the turret. To the left is the rear of two 6-volt storage batteries. To the right is the power charger, as the gasoline engine that drove the generator was called. On the rear of the power charger is the rope-pull starter. Above the engine is the fuel tank, and to the left of the engine is the air cleaner. (ATHS)*

Above: *Multiple Gun Motor Carriage M16 registration number 4049979 and Ordnance number 1746 was photographed as part of Project 243 of the Ordnance Operation, General Motors Proving Ground, on 31 August 1943. This was an early-production example of the M16 from Quartermaster W-303-ORD-1860. (Patton Museum)* **Below:** *Photographed on 31 August 1943 at the General Motors Milford Proving Ground, M16 registration number 4049979 has been fitted with a canvas cover of the winch. A one-foot square grid was superimposed on the image by the Proving Ground photographer, giving us an excellent idea of the size of the vehicle and the relative placement of its components. (TACOM LCMC History Office)*

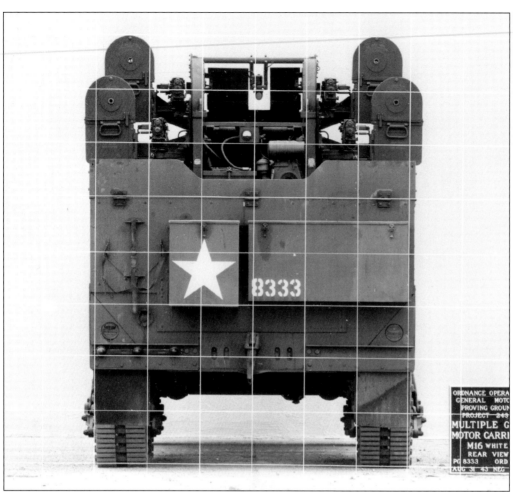

Left: *The M16 is seen from the rear, showing the relative sizes of the two storage boxes on the rear of the body. The number 8333, seen at several places on this vehicle, is this half-track's GM Proving Ground number. Note how the .50-caliber ammunition chests jut out slightly beyond the sides of the body. (Patton Museum)*

Below: *The same Multiple Gun Motor Carriage M16 is viewed from the left rear at the General Motors Proving Ground. Three nonstandard, dome-shaped objects, possibly small lights, are attached to the left bumperette. (Patton Museum)*

Above: *Multiple Gun Motor Carriage M16 registration number 4049979 is seen from the left side in a photograph taken at the GM Proving Ground on 31 August 1943. This vehicle had Goodyear tires, size 8.25-20, although tires from Firestone, General, Goodrich and Seiberling also were used on these half-tracks. (Patton Museum)*

Right: *The same M16 is seen from the front. Behind the front bumper on this vehicle was a Tulsa Model 18G winch with a capacity of 10,000 pounds. Also in view is the upper part of the shield of the turret, including the two folding flat plates to the sides of the gun sight. (Patton Museum)*

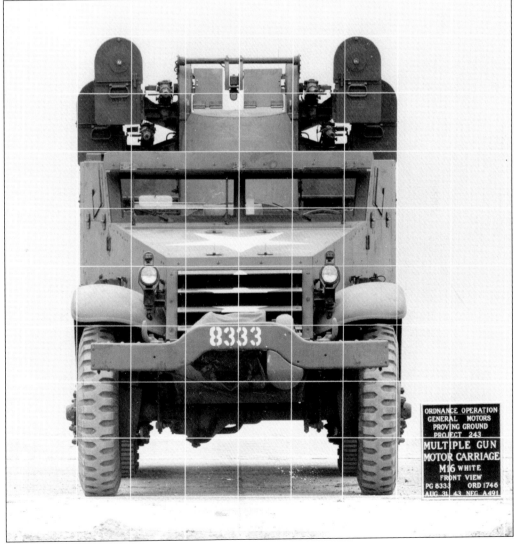

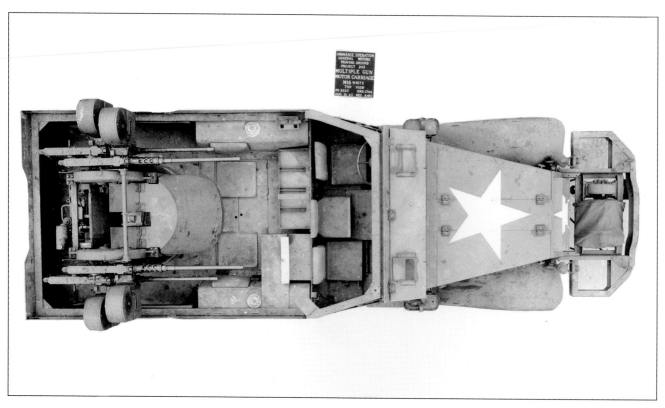

Above: *An overhead view of Multiple Gun Motor Carriage M16 registration number 4049979 shows the fighting-compartment layout: fuel tanks and inboard-facing seats to the front, with a rack for four .50-caliber ammunition chests between the tanks, and the turret to the rear, with very little working space for crewmen to the sides and the rear of the turret.*
Below: *The dashboard and steering wheel of Multiple Gun*

Motor Carriage M16 registration number 4049979 are shown. Of the two large instruments, the one on the left is the instrument cluster, containing an ammeter, fuel gauge, temperature gauge, and oil-pressure gauge; and the instrument on the right is the speedometer with an odometer and a trip odometer. Both of these instruments were made by Stewart-Warner. (Patton Museum, both)

Above: *Multiple Gun Motor Carriage M16 Ordnance number 2654 was photographed during analysis at the Ordnance Operation, Engineering Standards Vehicle Laboratory, Detroit, Michigan, on 8 February 1944. Above the front right corner of the fighting compartment is a radio antenna mount. A rolled camouflage net wrapped in a tarpaulin is stored on the right fender. (Patton Museum)*

Right: *The same M16, Ordnance number 2654, is seen from the rear at the Ordnance Operation, Engineering Standards Vehicle Laboratory, Detroit. A metal bucket is strapped to the left rear of the vehicle; below it is a receptacle and cover for an electrical connection for a trailer. (Patton Museum)*

Above: M16 Ordnance number 2654 is seen from the left in an 8 February 1944 photograph. Features that differentiate the M16 from the related International Harvester Multiple Gun Motor Carriage M17 include square vertical corners at the rear of the body, side folding panels that extended to the rear corners of the body, and more complex fenders that had curved lateral profiles as well as skirts to the rears of the wheels. (Patton Museum) **Below:** Multiple Gun Motor Carriage M16. With the folding upper panel of the fighting compartment in the lowered position, the two spare headlight assemblies are visible in their stowed positions to the rear of the cab. (TACOM LCMC History Office)

Above: *International Harvester produced 1,000 Multiple Gun Motor Carriages M17 based on the M5 half-track personnel carrier. Shown here is M17 registration number 40175789 Like the International Harvester Multiple Gun Motor Carriage M14 with twin .50-caliber machine guns, the folding rear panel of the fighting compartment of the M17 was located several inches to the front of the rear of the compartment, with correspondingly* shorter folding side panels, to compensate for the rounded rear corners of the body. (Wisconsin Historical Society) **Below:** *The IH Multiple Gun Motor Carriage M17 had the same .50-caliber Multiple Machine Gun Mount M45D as the Multiple Gun Motor Carriage M16. The folding side and rear plates of the fighting compartment were cut out to provide clearance for the ammunition chests. (Wisconsin Historical Society)*

Above: *Whereas the Multiple Gun Motor Carriage M16 had two separate storage boxes on the rear of the body, the M17 had one large box. The M17s were assigned U.S. Army registration numbers 40175244 to 40176243 and serial numbers 1 to 1000. (Wisconsin Historical Society)*

Left: *A crowbar was stored on holders on the rear of the rear stowage box of the Multiple Gun Motor Carriage M17. A bucket holder was to the left of that box, and below the box were the tow pintle and two bumperettes made of curved steel. (Wisconsin Historical Society)*

Above: *An IH Multiple Gun Motor Carriage M17 is observed from the left. The Soviets were assigned the entire run of M17s, and production of these vehicles lasted from December 1943 to March 1944. (Wisconsin Historical Society)* **Below:** *As seen on International Harvester Multiple Gun Motor Carriage M17 registration number 40175789, the M17s had the sliding visors and guides on the insides of the cab doors, whereas the White-manufactured Multiple Gun Motor Carriage M16 had the sliding visors and guides on the outsides of the cab doors. (Patton Museum)*

Above: The quad .50-caliber machine guns of the M45D mount are at maximum elevation of +90 degrees. Minimum elevation was -10 degrees. Each of the Browning .50-caliber HB M2 machine guns had a rate of fire of between 450 and 575 rounds per minute, so together the four guns could fire around 2,000 rounds per minute. (Wisconsin Historical Society)

Left: An M17 is viewed from the front with the armored slats that protected the radiator from shrapnel in the open position. The quad .50-caliber machine guns could be fired over the windshield but only at an elevation of no less than approximately 0 degrees. (Wisconsin Historical Society)

Above: *In its continuing investigations into ways to bring more mobile antiaircraft firepower into the field, the Army experimented with a multiple gun mount the U.S. Navy developed in 1942 for possible use on PT boats. A Half-Track Car M2, registration number 4012073, was fitted with an Elco Turret B6, nicknamed the Thunderbolt. The turret had four 20mm Oerlikon automatic guns and two Browning M2 HB .50-caliber machine guns. (PT Boat Museum)*

Right: *The Elco Thunderbolt turret had a traverse of 360 degrees and an elevation range of +85 to -15 degrees. The gun tub was mounted on a yoke, with hydraulic cylinders tilting the tub up or down in order to achieve elevation. The tub of the turret had ½-inch armor plate on the front and ¼-inch armor on the sides and the rear. What seems to have been a generator was mounted above the battery box on the right fender. (PT Boat Museum)*

Above: *The Elco Thunderbolt on the M2 half-track is traversed to the right, and the guns are at approximately 45 degrees elevation. The head of the gunner, who sat in the left side of the turret, is visible. To the front of the gunner's face is the gun sight. (Jim Mesko collection)*

Left: *The M2 half-track with the experimental Elco Thunderbolt mount had cut-down side and rear panels on the fighting compartment and an extended rear end. Two semi-circular openings on each side of the crew compartment were presumably for clearing out the spent casings. Here, the left side of the yoke that supported the gun bucket is visible, along with the left hydraulic cylinder for elevating the tub and guns. (Jim Mesko collection)*

Above: *With the Elco Thunderbolt elevated, the arrangement of the four 20mm guns and, to the sides, the .50-caliber machine guns are apparent. The gunner's seat and controls were to the left rear of the tub. The gunner controlled the movement of the mount with control grips to his front. Each of the 20mm guns received ammunition from a 60-round magazine. To the sides of the sidewalls of the tub are the hydraulic elevating cylinders. (Jim Mesko collection)*

Right: *In September 1941, four pilot half-track multiple gun motor carriages to include a mount containing an automatic 37mm Gun M1A2 and two Browning .50-caliber HB machine guns were assembled for the Coast Artillery. These vehicles were designated the Multiple Gun Motor Carriage T28, and tests on them commenced at Aberdeen Proving Ground in October 1941. The side and rear armor of the fighting compartment was removed to provide clearance for the multiple gun mount. Seen in this photo is the pilot vehicle based on M2 registration number W-4012073 / Ordnance number 1875. This vehicle had a rotating platform for the gun mount but lacked the .50-caliber machine guns. (NARA)*

Above: *In this view of T28 pilot W-4012073 from the left side at Aberdeen Proving Ground on 7 October 1941, the .50-caliber machine guns are installed on the gun mount. These machine guns were equipped with water-cooling jackets and were fed from M2 ammunition chests. The 37mm cannon was between and below the machine guns. (NARA)*

Left: *The guns of T28 pilot registration number W-4012073 are at 0 degrees traverse and 45 degrees elevation. The guns were mounted on a modified mount that employed the upper part of the 37mm Gun Carriage M3E1. There was a seat and hand controls for the elevation operator, right, and for the traversing operator, left. Each operator had two hand wheels, oriented fore-and-aft. (NARA)*

Right: *Another of the four Multiple Gun Motor Carriages T28, registration number W-4012056 / Ordnance number 1858, was built without a rotating platform for the gun mount. The 37mm gun is dismounted in this photo, but the twin .50-caliber machine guns and their M2 ammunition chests are in place. The gun mount is traversed to the front. (NARA)*

Below: *The same T28, USA W-4102056, is seen from the right side with all three guns mounted, at Aberdeen Proving Ground on 3 October 1941. Both the elevation and traverse systems of the gun mount were hand-operated, two-speed types, with one turn of the hand wheel respectively traversing or elevating the guns 3.75 degrees in the slow ratio and 11.25 degrees in the fast ratio. (Kevin Emdee collection)*

The guns of T28 registration number W-4102073 / Ordnance number 1875, the vehicle with the rotating platform on the gun mount, are at maximum elevation of 85 degrees. Minimum elevation was 0 degrees. The gun mount's fire-control equipment consisted of a Sighting System M2 and a Telescope M7. (NARA)

Multiple Gun Motor Carriage T28 registration number W-4102073 is seen in at Aberdeen Proving Ground, Maryland, on 7 October 1941 with its guns in the travel position. The 37mm gun had a rate of fire of 120 rounds per minute, while each of the .50-caliber machine guns had a rate of fire of up to 650 rounds per minute. (NARA)

Above: *Some features are present in this 11 October 1941 photo of Multiple Gun Motor Carriage T28 registration number W-4102073 that aren't present in the 7 October 1941 photos of the vehicle at Aberdeen. Two changes visible here are a third seat on the gun mount and a riveted metal box to the side of the fuel tank behind the cab. The photo was taken in Washington, D.C., during a demonstration of Army vehicles. (NARA)*

Right: *The new storage box, possibly for 37mm ammunition, behind the left side of the cab of T28 W-4102073 is seen close-up. Note the dark, glossy paint on the box compared to the duller, lighter-colored Olive Drab paint on the half-track. (NARA)*

Above: *The modified T28 registration number W-4102073 also had two tractor-type crew seats with back rests added to the top of the fuel tank. Now, there also were storage provisions for two M2 ammunition chests to the right of the fuel tank. The chests were secured with a webbing strap. At the top is the right .50-caliber machine gun with its water-cooling jacket. (NARA)*

Below: *Three GIs are manning the gun mount of T28 regis-*

tration number W-4102073 as modified following the 1941 Aberdeen tests. Immediately under the 37mm gun barrel is the gun's recuperator assembly. The separate cylinder below the 37mm gun and just above the rotating platform is the equilibrator, which acted to counterbalance the forward-heavy guns in order to make it easier to elevate and depress them. (Kevin Emdee collection)

Above: *The same Multiple Gun Motor Carriage T28 is viewed from the right rear. The ammunition chests are not mounted on the .50-caliber machine guns. Ammunition was fed to the 37mm gun by means of 10-round clips. The clips were fed into the left side of the feed box; the spent casings were ejected through the bottom of the receiver, and the spent clip was ejected through the right side of the feed box. (Kevin Emdee collection)* **Below:** *The guns are traversed forward and at are at approximately full elevation, +85 degrees, on the Multiple Gun Motor Carriage T28 W-4102060 during the demonstration in Washington. From this angle, two additional multiple 37mm and twin .50-caliber gun mounts are visible in the background. (NARA)*

The rear of the multiple gun mount of T28 registration number W-4102060 is shown. The positions of the three crew seats, including the raised center one, are visible. On a small platform at the rear of the rotating platform are two boxes with a hand crank to the rears. These are Water Chests M3 for supplying cooling water to the machine guns. The handles drove pumps that circulated cooling water to the .50-caliber machine guns and the 37mm gun. (NARA)

Right: The same multiple gun mount is seen from a different angle. One of the Water Chests M3 was used for cooling the 37mm gun; it was necessary to flow clean water through the barrel of the gun after heavy, sustained firing. Among the mechanisms in the view is the Sighting System M2, a direct-aiming system with a crossbar to hold two tracking telescopes that moved in unison with the elevation and azimuth of the guns. (NARA)

Below: The guns of T28 registration number W-4102060 are at approximately maximum elevation in another 11 October 1941 photograph. Above and aft of the .50-caliber ammunition chests is the crossbar of the Sighting System M2 that supports, on each end, a tracking telescope. Mounted on the interior of the right side of the gun shield is an inward facing, tractor-type crew seat. (NARA)

Left: *Details of the crew seats of the multiple gun mount of T28 W-410206U are shown, including the support for the center seat. The backrest of each seat was equipped with a cushion that was lashed in place. Above the backrest of the center seat is the support bar for the tracking telescopes. At the bottom are the two M3 water chests; to the right is a hand-hold in the rear of the left side of the gun shield. (NARA)*

Below: *Although the Coast Artillery Board cancelled the Multiple Gun Motor Carriage T28 project in April 1942, two months later the Army developed a requirement for dual-purpose antiaircraft/antitank vehicles for the upcoming North Africa Campaign. Under Ordnance contract W-670-ORD-2627, in July and August 1942 Autocar converted 80 M3 personnel-carrier half-tracks to multiple-gun motor carriages by installing combination 37mm and twin-.50-caliber gun mounts. These were designated the T28E1, an example of which is depicted here. (TACOM LCMC History Office)*

Above: *The first Multiple Gun Motor Carriage T28E1 is shown with its guns fully elevated during tests at Aberdeen Proving Ground on 31 August 1942. The gun mount had a rotating platform with angular edges. Ammunition chests are stowed on the rear corner of the platform. To each side of the fuel tank is a storage chest for 37mm ammunition clips, and to the rear of each of these chests is a .50-caliber ammunition chest. (Steve Zaloga collection)*

Right: *After the Coast Artillery Board cancelled the Multiple Gun Motor Carriage T28 project in April 1942, the Board decided by December of that year to pursue instead a half-track with a quad .50-caliber Machine Gun M2 mount. The United Shoe Machinery Company designed two different mounts, the Machine Gun Mount T60 and the Machine Gun Mount T60E1. Two each of these mounts were installed on four pilot half-track multiple gun motor carriages: the T37 (with the T60 mount, as seen here) and the T37E1 (with the T60E1 mount). (TACOM LCMC History Office)*

Left: *On the Machine Gun Mount T60, the two top .50-caliber machine guns were outboard of the two bottom guns; this order was reversed on the Machine Gun Mount T60E1. Both types of mounts were based on the upper part of the 37mm Gun Carriage M3E1, the same mount used on the Multiple Gun Motor Carriage T28. This elevated view of the T60 mount was taken at Aberdeen Proving Ground on 23 June 1942. (Patton Museum)*

Below: *This photo from the front end of a Machine Gun Mount T60 on a Multiple Gun Motor Carriage T37 was taken at Aberdeen Proving Ground on 26 June 1942 to illustrate the trapezoidal lay-out of the machine guns as viewed from the front. Because of the tight arrangement of the guns, there was not enough room to mount ammunition chests on the guns. Instead, the chests were positioned on the mount plat-form, two per side, from which the ammo was fed to the guns. (Patton Museum)*

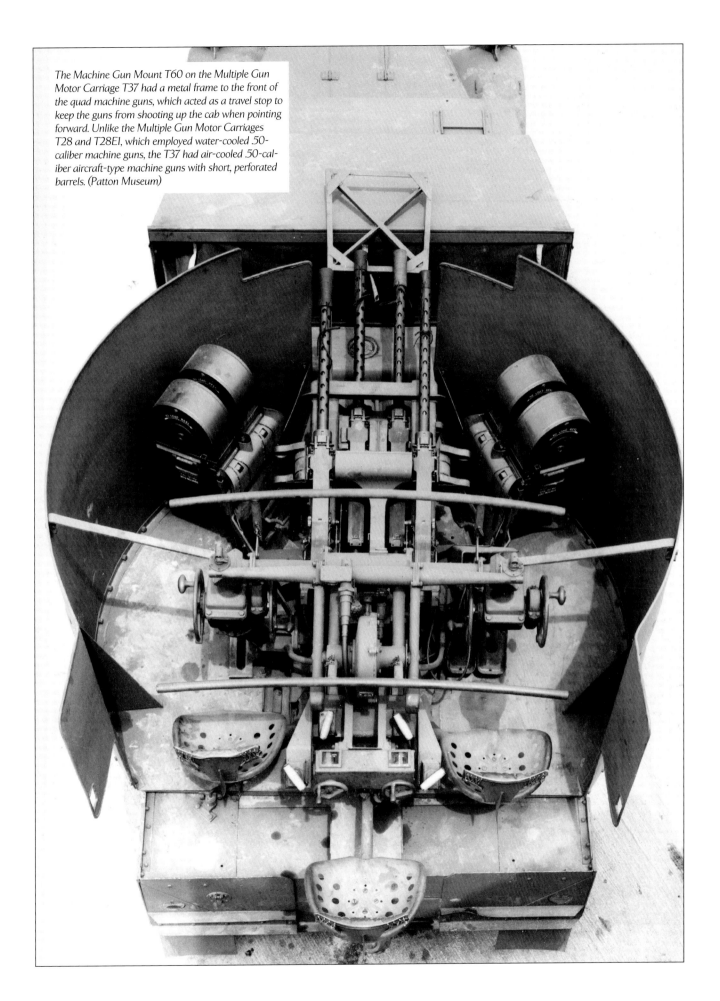

The Machine Gun Mount T60 on the Multiple Gun Motor Carriage T37 had a metal frame to the front of the quad machine guns, which acted as a travel stop to keep the guns from shooting up the cab when pointing forward. Unlike the Multiple Gun Motor Carriages T28 and T28E1, which employed water-cooled .50-caliber machine guns, the T37 had air-cooled .50-caliber aircraft-type machine guns with short, perforated barrels. (Patton Museum)

Left: *The crewman in the center seat of the Machine Gun Mount T60 had these controls in front of him. There were four cocking handles for the .50-caliber machine guns, and also the deflection transmitter, part of the fire-control system for leading the target. The latter constituted a hand wheel and indicator for left and right deflection (left) and a hand wheel and indicator for vertical deflection (right). (Patton Museum)*

Below: *This Multiple Gun Motor Carriage T37 was photographed at Aberdeen Proving Ground a year and a half after the end of World War II, on 18 February 1947. The frame for keeping the machine guns from firing into the cab is jutting to the front of the turret. The .50-caliber guns evidently were not mounted at this time. The curved shield for the gun mount was formed from 0.5-inch armor. (US Army Ordnance Museum)*

Above: *In addition to creating the Machine Gun Mount T60 for the two pilot Multiple Gun Motor Carriages T37, the United Shoe Machinery Company also designed and built two examples of the Machine Gun Mount T60E1, and these were installed on the Multiple Gun Motor Carriage T37E1. One of those two vehicles, based on a Half-Track Car M2, U.S. Army registration number W-402005, is seen here during testing at Aberdeen Proving* Ground *on 22 June 1942.* **Below:** *With the machine guns hidden behind the armor shield of the gun mount, the T37E1 looked virtually identical to the T37. The major difference was that the four air-cooled Browning M2 .50-caliber machine guns of the T37 were arranged in two tiers, while the .50-caliber machine guns of the T37E1 were positioned straight across on the same level.* (NARA, both)

Left: *As seen from the rear, the T60E1 gun mount, like the T60 mount, had as its basis the upper part of the 37mm Gun Carriage M3E1 and had three seats, although the center seat of the T60E1 lacks a backrest in this photo. Unlike the T60 mount, the T60E1 included two racks to the sides of the center seat for M2 .50-caliber ammunition chests for feeding the two middle guns. (NARA)*

Below: *The T60E1 mount of the Multiple Gun Motor Carriage T37E1 had a traverse of 360 degrees and a range of elevation from +85 to -5 degrees. Visible to the front of the center seat of the gun mount is the deflection transmitter, with its hand wheel for setting the horizontal and the vertical deflection. (NARA)*

Right: *Although all four .50-caliber machine guns of the Multiple Gun Motor Carriage T37E1 were on the same level, the two outboard guns jutted to the front of the two middle guns. Dust covers are secured to the machine gun barrels. The middle crewman's seat lacked a backrest presumably for ease of access due to the proximity of the two ammunition chests stored next to the seat. (NARA)*

Below: *As seen in an Aberdeen Proving Ground photograph dated 22 June 1942, the four Browning M2 .50-caliber machine guns of the Multiple Gun Motor Carriage T37E1 were fed by feed chutes from M2 ammunition chests that were not directly attached to the machine guns. The chests for the outboard guns were to the outboard sides of the gun receivers. (NARA)*

Above: *A Multiple Gun Motor Carriage T37E1 is seen from the left side at Aberdeen Proving Ground on 22 June 1942. During tests, the ammunition feeds for the machine guns were found to be unreliable, and there were problems with controlling the guns that proved to be insoluble. The T37/T37E1 project was cancelled in favor of the M13, M14, and M15 multiple gun carriages on 8 January 1943. (NARA)* **Below:** *After the Antiaircraft Artillery Board rejected the Multiple Gun Motor Carriage T28,* the Board elected to proceed with an improved version of the vehicle based on the Half-track Personnel Carrier M3 and featuring air-cooled Browning M2 HB .50-caliber machine guns instead of water-cooled .50s, along with other modifications. The vehicle was designated the Half-Track Multiple Gun Motor Carriage M15 and it entered production as a Substitute Standard vehicle. Six hundred examples were delivered. (From the collections of The Henry Ford Museum)

Above: *A Half-Track Multiple Gun Motor Carriage M15 is seen from the left rear, showing the arrangement of the three seats in the gun mount. The elevation and azimuth control hand wheels were oriented vertically, parallel to the guns, and were mounted in pairs.* **Below:** *The combination gun mount on the Half-Track Multiple Gun Motor Carriage M15 was designated the M42, and, in addition to the two Browning M2 HB .50-caliber machine guns, it included a 37mm Gun M1A2. The three gun barrels protruded through a flat armor shield that moved in unison with the elevation or depression of the guns. This was in addition to the shield around the front and sides of the gun mount. Seen here is the first M15 to be delivered, registration number 4083287, at Aberdeen Proving Ground on 16 December 1942. (NARA, both)*

Above: *Half-Track Multiple Gun Motor Carriage M15 registration number 4083287, built by Autocar, is seen from the right rear during tests at Aberdeen Proving Ground on 16 December 1942. The shield of the Combination Gun Mount M42 was not a carbon copy of the shield used on the M15's predecessor, the T28, having a different shape and lacking the latter's handholds on the rear of the shield. (NARA)*

Left: *The elevation and azimuth hand wheels of the Gun Mount M42 were in pairs and were vertically oriented. Ammunition chests were stored on the platform, four on each side. On the inside of the gun shield were cases for storing 37mm ammunition clips. A carbine was in a bracket on each side of the front of the shield. Note the V-shaped support for the moveable frontal shield attached to the gun mount. (NARA)*

Right: *This rear view of a Multiple Gun Motor Carriage M15 was taken at the Autocar factory in Ardmore, Pennsylvania, on 8 December 1942. Note the various boxes and cases on the rear of the platform of the gun mount and the 37mm ammunition storage boxes on the inner sides of the shield. (From the collections of The Henry Ford Museum)*

Below: *An official Autocar photo of a Multiple Gun Motor Carriage M15 shows the open rear of the gun-mount shield, along with the three operators' seats and some of the sighting mechanism. To the front of the main shield, a glimpse of the small shield affixed to the front of the guns is available. (From the collections of The Henry Ford Museum)*

Left: *The twin .50-caliber machine guns and the 37mm gun of the Multiple Gun Motor Carriage M15 are elevated, showing the positioning of the shield mounted to the front of the guns. As can be seen, this shield was rather pointless, as it would have provided the crew with negligible protection from attack from above. (From the collections of The Henry Ford Museum)*

Below: *The same Half-Track Multiple Gun Motor Carriage M15 is seen from the right side at the Autocar factory in December 1942. The guns are at approximately 45 degrees elevation. On the next iteration of the half-track combination gun carriage, the M15E1, the frontal shield attached to the guns would be eliminated. (From the collections of The Henry Ford Museum)*

Above: *The gun mount of the Half-Track Multiple Gun Motor Carriage M15 is traversed to the right. If the opening at the front of the gun-mount shield can be considered to form a T shape, the leg of the T constituted an opening for the equilibrator, while the top of the T provided clearance for the gun barrels. (From the collections of The Henry Ford)*

Right: *This official Autocar photo of the front of a Half-Track Multiple Gun Motor Carriage M15 provides a good view of the shape and relative size of the small shield on the front of the guns. This shield provided a degree of added protection to the gun crew and the guns at the expense of forward visibility. (From the collections of The Henry Ford)*

Above: *The original Aberdeen Proving Ground caption to this photo states that it shows a "Multiple Gun Motor Carriage, M15 (modified)" of Project 6-2-6-2 on 13 January 1943. The moveable front shield of the gun mount had been removed, ostensibly to allow better visibility. There now was a handhold at the center of the side shield.* **Below:** *The modified Multiple*

Gun Motor Carriage M15 now had a storage chest on the rack to the rear of the center seat of the gun mount. There was another equipment chest with two handles, inset into the rear of the body above the tow pintle. On each side of the vehicle to the rear of the cab was a storage box with a seat cushion and seatbelt on top. (NARA, both)

Right: *The modified Multiple Gun Motor Carriage M15 is seen from the rear during tests at Aberdeen Proving Ground on 13 January 1943. Note how the storage chest on the rear of the platform of the gun mount is offset to the left of center. To the front of the crew seats are the control hand wheels, the supports for the gun sights, and diagonal braces for the side armor. (NARA)*

Below: *Based on the Multiple Gun Motor Carriage M15's satisfactory service, the Army sought further production of the vehicle, but there was a shortage of gun mounts. A substitute mount based on the 37mm Gun Carriage M3A1 was developed and standardized as the Combination Gun Mount M54. Half-tracks armed with this mount were designated the Combination Gun Motor Carriage M15A1, and an example is shown here in a photo dated 30 November 1943. Weatherproof covers are installed over the cab and the gun mount. (Patton Museum)*

Above: *On the Combination Gun Motor Carriage M15A1, there were hinged panels on the diagonal forward facets of the gun shield; these could be lowered, as shown here, to provide improved visibility to the gun crew. To solve the problem of the guns accidentally shooting the cab or the engine compartment, a curved rail was installed above the upper rear of the cab. (Patton Museum)*

Left: *The Combination Gun Mount M54 of a Combination Gun Motor Carriage M15A1 is seen from the upper rear. Two M2 .50-caliber ammunition chests are stored to each side of the middle seat. The control hand wheels of the Multiple Gun Motor Carriage M15 had been replaced by hand cranks, as seen to the front of the right seat. With the new gun shield with folding forward panels, now there was room for only three 37mm ammunition boxes on each side of the shield. (Patton Museum)*

Above: *The Swedish-designed Bofors 40mm automatic gun had gained a reputation by the early part of World War II as a potent and dependable antiaircraft weapon, capable of firing a high-explosive shell that could knock down virtually any aircraft at low altitude or knock out lightly armored vehicles. Chrysler built a version of the gun for the U.S. Army, and the Army decided in late June 1942 to experiment with mounting a 40mm Gun M1 on a 40mm Gun Mount T5 installed on an M3 half-track. Two pilots were made, designated the 40mm Gun Motor* Carriage T54, and one of them, registration number W-4028245, is depicted in an Aberdeen Proving Ground photo dated 14 July 1942. (Kevin Emdee collection) **Below:** *One of two prototype 40mm Gun Motor Carriages T54 is seen with a cover installed over the gun mount. This cover was officially referred to as the Crawford Zipper Mount Cover. A separate cover is over the gun muzzle. Speed-ring sights are installed on the sight support, and there are even fabric covers installed over the front and the rear rings of these sights. (Patton Museum)*

Left: *The 40mm Gun Mount T5 on a 40mm Gun Motor Carriage T54 is viewed from the rear in a 14 July 1942 Aberdeen Proving Ground image. The backrests of the gun crew seats have lashed-on cushions. At the rear of the gun receiver is the downward-curved spent-casing deflector, which directed casings into a mating spent-casing chute below it. On that deflector is a reflector, directly between the seat pans of the gun mount. (NARA)*

Below: *During testing at Aberdeen Proving Ground, the 40mm Gun Motor Carriage T54 is viewed from the right rear with a Crawford Zipper Mount Cover installed over the 40mm Gun Mount T5. The cover extended over the barrel support at the front end of the gun receiver. (NARA)*

Above: *The 40mm Gun Motor Carriage T54 at Aberdeen Proving Ground has the Crawford cover removed from the 40mm gun mount in this 14 July 1942 image. Below the rear of the barrel of the gun is the recoil cylinder; below that feature and projecting from the front of the gun carriage is the right of two equilibrator cylinders. (NARA)*

Right: *In a frontal view of the 40mm Gun Motor Carriage T54, the conical flash suppressor on the muzzle makes the barrel seem larger than it actually was. A lateral tube on top of the gun's receiver held the gun sights. To the rear of the tube on top of the receiver is a cover over the auto-loading mechanism. (NARA)*

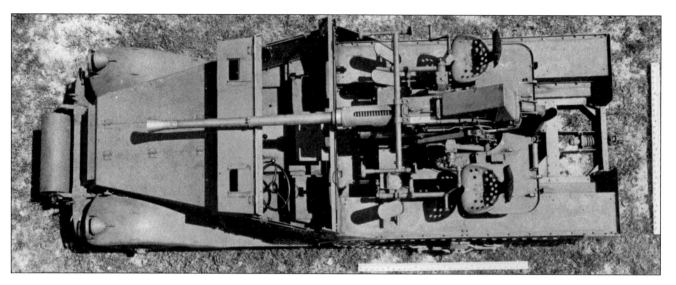

Above: The 40mm Gun Motor Carriage T54 is seen from above. To the left of the gun sat the elevation operator, who used a hand crank to elevate or depress the gun. He also fired the gun using a foot pedal. To the right of the gun was the seat for the azimuth operator, who traversed the piece using a hand crank. On the 40mm Gun MI, there also was a firing pedal that the loader could use, to the left rear of the gun. (NARA)

Below: At first glance, this half-track with a 40mm gun mount would appear to be a Half-Track 40mm Gun Motor Carriage T54, but is has the wrong U.S.A. number (4027132), and the gun mount is lower than that of the T54, which was raised several inches off the deck. The gun mount lacks the attributes of the other "official" half-track 40mm GMCs, so it remains unclear if this vehicle was a special conversion or something else. (NARA)

Above: *The same half-track 40mm GMC is seen from another angle during firing tests along a shoreline. In the background are what appear to be a mix of U.S. and British army personnel.*

Below: *The 40mm gun is firing toward the water on the same GMC while loaders prepare to insert more ammunition clips into the auto-loader on top of the gun's receiver. (NARA, both)*

Above: Tests of the 40mm Gun Motor Carriage T54 disclosed that the vehicle was unstable, in part because of the height of the gun mount above the floor. Thus, a 40mm Gun M1 on a shorter mount was installed in an armored tub on an M3 half-track personnel carrier, registration number W-4028252. This vehicle was designated the 40mm Gun Motor Carriage T54E1, and it is seen in an Aberdeen Proving Ground photo dated 12 October 1942. Note the groove in the top of the windshield frame to allow clearance for the barrel of the lowered 40mm gun. **Below:** To stabilize the 40mm GMC T54E1 during static firing, an outrigger was mounted at each corner of the fighting compartment. The tubes of the outriggers are seen here in the travel position. Visible above the tub is the wedge-shaped cover for the 40mm gun's auto-feeder. Jutting from the rear of the gun tub was a holder for a 16-round ammunition box, not installed here. At the rear of the vehicle was a locker with rear doors. (NARA, both)

Above: The 40mm Gun M1 is elevated to 45 degrees in this photo of the 40mm Gun Motor Carriage T54E1. Curved cutouts on the front of the tub were for sighting purposes. The 16-round 40mm ammunition case is installed on top of the rear of the tub. Details of the top of the locker at the rear of the vehicle and the hard top of the cab are visible. It has been speculated that the objects stored in the rack above the front roller may have been base plates for screw jacks for stabilizing the vehicle dur-

ing firing, but that assertion has not been verified. (NARA)
Below: This heavily retouched photo is a depiction of the 40mm Gun Motor Carriage T54E1 with the outriggers deployed to stabilize the gun mount while firing from a fixed position. Base plates have been fitted to the outer ends of the outriggers, and stakes have been driven through the plates to secure them to the ground. An ammunition trailer is hitched to the half-track. (TACOM LCMC History Office)

Above: *The Army undertook experiments with the 40mm Gun Motor Carriage T59. This pilot was based on the same M3 half-track chassis as the T54E1, registration number W-4028252, except that the T59 was equipped with a remote-control director in a Half-Track Instrument Carrier T18. (TACOM LCMC History Office)* **Below:** *One of two prototype 40mm Gun Motor Carriages T54, registration number W-*4028245, was repurposed as a 40mm Gun Motor Carriage T59 by the time this photo was taken at Aberdeen Proving Ground on 14 April 1943. There was nothing in its outward appearance to differentiate it from a T54E1. Leveling jacks were mounted on heavy-duty brackets at the lower corners of the rear of the vehicle; to deploy the jacks they were released and swung down. (NARA)*

Above: *A 40mm GMC M59 (modified) with the armored tub removed from the gun mount is deployed for firing at Aberdeen Proving Ground on 12 March 1943. The outriggers are extended and staked to the ground, and the two screw jacks at the rear of the vehicle are deployed. The 40mm gun is traversed 90 degrees to the right and is at 0 degrees elevation. (Jim Gilmore collection)* **Below:** *In a further effort to solve the stability prob-lems of the 40mm half-track GMCs, this 40mm Gun Motor Carriage M59, seen at Aberdeen Proving Ground on 2 August 1943, has been further modified by the addition of revised out-riggers to the sides of the bogie assemblies. The left outrigger is seen here in the raised position, with its base plate removed. In addition, an outrigger for supporting and leveling the front end has been mounted on the center of the front bumper. (NARA)*

Above: A 40mm GMC M59 is shown with the modified outriggers deployed. The base plate of the right outrigger has sunk into the ground, but its two grab handles are visible. The gusseted base plate of the front outrigger is visible; note the oblong slots cut into the gussets to form handholds. The front roller had been removed to provide space for the screw jack. **Below:** A right-rear view of a modified 40mm Gun Motor Carriage M59 shows the rear and the right outriggers in their travel positions. The outrigger arms have been secured with chains. To the front of the right seat of the gun mount is the oil gear for the powered traversing mechanism. Oil gears for power traversing and elevating the guns were an integral part of the remote-control firing system of the 40mm GMC M59. (Jim Gilmore collection, both)

Above: *A 40mm GMC M59 (modified) is set up in a firing position during tests at Aberdeen Proving Ground on 23 July 1943. All four of the outriggers were adjusted and leveled with hand-operated screws. The side and rear outriggers had round base plates with two grab handles. A measuring stick is propped up in front of the front wheel for scale reference.* **Below:** *The*

40mm Gun Motor Carriage T59E1 was the T59 with the armored tub removed and flat armor plates installed around the fighting compartment. An example, registration number 4019506, is seen during tests at Aberdeen on 17 June 1943. Note the early-style outriggers and the travel lock for the 40mm gun barrel on the top rear of the cab. (NARA, both)

Above: *In a top view of a 40mm Gun Motor Carriage T59E1, to the rear of the 40mm gun is a rack for an ammunition case. Arranged around the body armor of the fighting compartment are holders for 40mm ammunition clips. Two storage boxes are in the front corners of the fighting compartment. Below the rear of the gun is the curved spent-cartridge chute. (Patton Museum)*

Below: *The early-type outriggers and rear jacks are extended and staked to the ground on this 40mm Gun Motor Carriage T59E1 at Aberdeen on 29 June 1943. Ostensibly the gap between the upper and the lower plates on the sides and rear of the body were to allow spent 40mm casings to be pushed off the floor around the gun mount. (NARA)*

Above: *In a further improvement of the 40mm GMC T54E1, experiments were made with mounting two .50-caliber M2 machine guns coaxially with the 40mm Gun M1. The resulting vehicle was designated the 40mm Gun Motor Carriage T60. The right machine gun barrel is barely visible next to the 40mm gun barrel to the rear of the arrowed 40mm travel lock atop the windshield. The other white arrow to the rear of the right cab door indicates a fitting found on each side of the cab of the T54E1, T59, and T60, but not the T54. This constituted a bent* tube that swiveled on a bracket at the bottom, with a coil spring at the top, and may have been a bumper to cushion the blow when the 40mm gun was inadvertently traversed against the rear corner of the cab. **Below:** *From any angle from which the .50-caliber machine guns weren't visible, the 40mm GMC T60 appeared identical to a T54E1, right down to the early-type outriggers and jacks. The example shown here is registration number 4028245 and was photographed at Aberdeen Proving Ground on 9 February 1943. (NARA, both)*

Above: *The positioning of the .50-caliber machine guns next to the 40mm Gun M1 on the 40mm Gun Motor Carriage T60 is visible in this elevated view. The machine guns had the early-style barrel supports to the fronts of the receivers, with elongated cooling slots instead of the round openings that the later barrel supports had. A measuring stick is lying atop the left side of the gun tub.* **Below:** *The gun mount of the 40mm Gun Motor Carriage T60 is seen from the front. The unusual device attached to the gun and the left side of the gun-sight support is a*

Stiffkey Stick. This was a cheap but effective alternative to director equipment for calculating firing solutions against moving targets. The crew chief stood behind the Stiffkey Stick and held the horizontal bar at the top with handgrips and levers, aligning the stick with the target, clicking the hand lever once for each estimated speed of 50 miles per hour. The movement of the stick and the clicking of the lever was transmitted through cables to the gun layers' foresights, so all the layers had to do to track the aircraft was to keep it centered in their foresights. (NARA, both)

Above: *A Stiffkey Stick mounted on a 40mm Gun M1 on a T60 is viewed from the rear. At the center of the operator's handlebar is a horizontally oriented gauge or indicator. A hand lever for transmitting estimated target speed is adjacent to each grip on the handlebar. The bottom end of the right brace of the Stiffkey Stick was clamped to the 40mm gun.* **Below:** *Firing tests are underway on a 40mm Gun Motor Carriage T60 at* Aberdeen Proving Ground on 12 February 1943. The original caption for this photo points out deficiencies with the vehicle: there was not sufficient room for the operator of the Stiffkey Stick and for loading the .50-caliber machine guns. Here, with its cover removed, the automatic feed mechanism of the 40mm gun is visible, with a four-round clip of ammo in it. (NARA, both)

Left: *On 14 February 1943 a 40mm Gun Motor Carriage T60 is set up for firing at Aberdeen Proving Ground. The outriggers are extended and staked to the ground, and the screw jack attached to the front bumper is deployed. The direct-sights support bar has been removed from the gun mount. Note the type of ammunition boxes on the .50-caliber machine guns. (NARA)*

Below: *The same 40mm Gun Motor Carriage T60 is seen from the rear at Aberdeen on 14 February 1943 while being prepared for a firing test. A measuring stick is leaning against the rear of the vehicle. On this GMC, the tray for 40mm ready rounds is to the right side of the 40mm gun instead of in its usual position to the rear of the gun. (NARA)*

40mm Gun Motor Carriage T60 registration number 4019504 was photographed while stored outdoors at Aberdeen Proving Ground on 8 February 1947. The outriggers are folded up against the rear deck, a canvas cover is over the 40mm gun, and the .50-caliber machine guns apparently have been removed from the mount. (Ordnance Museum)

Not to be confused with the previously discussed Multiple Gun Motor Carriage T60E1, registration number W-401964, which featured a Martin twin .50-caliber machine gun turret, this Multiple Gun Motor Carriage T60E1 was armed with a 40mm Bofors gun with a Browning M2 HB .50-caliber machine gun to each side. It appears here at Aberdeen Proving Ground on 3 June 1943. Note the deployed outriggers and the jack installed under the front end. (NARA)

The Half-Track Instrument Carrier T18 was designed to accompany 40mm gun motor carriages in the field. Based on a Half-Track Personnel Carrier M3, it featured a hardtop cab and an extra-tall, open-topped armored enclosure behind the cab, inside which was a director: an instrument used to track a target aircraft and calculate a firing solution. Through the director, a 40mm gun on a half-track GMC could be aimed and fired remotely. This T18 bears registration number 4019509. (Patton Museum)

The same Half-Track Instrument Carrier T18 is seen from the front in an Aberdeen Proving Ground photograph dated 16 March 1949. The director appears to have been a Director M5 or a sub-model of it. This was the standard director for the 40mm Gun M1. Two observers operated it by using telescopes on opposite sides of the device and turning hand wheels to keep the target within the crosshairs of their telescopes. The movement of the hand wheels operated a mechanical computer in the director that predicted the trajectory of the target, transmitting a firing solution to the 40mm gun so it could fire its shells accurately at a fast-moving plane. (US Army Ordnance Museum)

Above: *In April 1942 the U.S. Army Ordnance Department authorized the loan of two 40mm Guns M1 to the American Ordnance Corporation for use in a twin 40mm gun mount of their own design, to be installed on an M3 half-track. The corporation did this work at their own expense. The guns were configured one over the other. The resulting vehicle, designated the 40mm Gun Motor Carriage T68, was tested at Aberdeen Proving Ground, where this photo was taken on 19 December 1942. (NARA)*

Right: *The twin guns of the 40mm GMC T68 were mounted on cradles with trunnions at the rear that fit on the front of the gun mount. Elevation was effected by the up and down tilting of the equilibrator—the two cylinders above the top gun—which pulled the guns up or lowered them via drag links. Tests indicated that the T68 would need many modifications to make it satisfactory for operational service, and the Ordnance Department cancelled the project on 24 June 1943. (NARA)*

Chapter 5:
Field Modifications

Making the Most of GI Engineering

For as long as soldiers have been going into the field, they have modified their issued equipment. The modifications could range from simple personalization should as applying a name, to attempts at improving the utility of an item on an individual or crew basis, to Battalion, Corps or Army level modifications.

In this volume, various individual modifications can be readily seen in the chapter on Field Use. This chapter, however, will look at modifications created at the unit level.

The 2nd Armored Division had considerable experience with their half-tracks, from their training at Fort Benning to being among the first U.S. units in North Africa as part of Operation Torch.

After shifting from the Mediterranean to England in preparation of the invasion at Normandy, units of the 2nd Armored Division created some interesting half-track configurations.

The unit had deployed to North Africa with M6 tank destroyers, also known as the Dodge WC-55. These vehicles, armed with the M3 37mm gun, were not notably effective against the German armor encountered, and losses of the M6, whose only armor was the gun shield, were high. On 30 April 1943 Army Ground Forces recommended that the M6 be declared obsolete. Chrysler was issued production orders to produce kits which would allow the WC-55s held in depot stocks to be converted to WC-52 weapons carriers.

The 2nd Armored followed a similar pattern, removing the guns and mounts from those WC-55s

that had survived North Africa. Some of these mounts and guns were then installed in M2 half-track cars that went ashore in France with the 41st Armored Infantry.

The 41st Armored Infantry was one of the units that reconfigured their M4 Mortar Carriers as well. With these field modifications, the mortar fired forward over the cab and hood, like the newer, longer-bodied M21.

One of the most famed mass-conversions in the field however led to the creation of what has come to be known alternately as the "Wasp," or M16B. Colonel Charles G. Patterson, who had been assigned the job of being the Antiaircraft Artillery Officer of First Army by Omar Bradley was preparing his troops and equipment for the Normandy invasion.

Since North Africa, the Table of Organization and Equipment had authorized each Automatic Weapons battalion eight 40mm Bofors and eight M51 trailer-mounted quad .50-caliber mount. However, neither Colonel Patterson nor his automatic weapons staff officer Major Fred Jacks were impressed with the mobility of the sleek, low-slung M51.

Tipping the scales at 3½-tons, each of the M51s was assigned a GMC CCKW 2½-ton 6x6 as a prime mover. The CCKW was the backbone of the Army's tactical transport fleet, and owing to perpetual shortages of components, significantly axles, the trucks were in chronically short supply.

Upon learning that a number of M2 half-tracks would become surplus under a new Table of

A quad .50-caliber machine gun crew poses proudly for the camera. The Maxson turret was transplanted into an M2-type half-track chassis. The practice of placing this type of turret in an M2 chassis was an expedient, as the space in the fighting compartment was considerably less than in the M3-based M16 multiple gun motor carriage. Note the presence of a ring sight rather than the normal reflex sight. (NARA)

Organization and Equipment, which would shift armored infantry battalions from the M2 to the M3, a mutually beneficial arrangement was concocted between Patterson and Colonel John Bruce Medaris, First Army Ordnance Officer. Medaris's heavy maintenance companies went to work removing the M45 mounts and their spacer rings from the M51 trailers and installing them in the M2. The vehicle so created was referred to alternately as the M16B or Wasp.

These efforts provided the AAA units with a more mobile mounting for their weapons, while freeing up sorely-needed trucks for other uses.

While the factory-made M16 MGMC had folding armor plates at the top of the sides and rear to permit clearance of the guns, and utilized the M45D mount with attached cannoneers platform, Ordnance Part number 5700301, the field-produced M16B lacked both of these details.

While the First Army After Action reports indicates that 332 of these conversions were made, an article written by Colonel Patterson himself appearing in the January-February 1949 edition of *Antiaircraft Journal* says:

"Half of the M-51's were converted to modified M-16's, called "Wasps." Col. J. B. Medaris, Army Ordnance Officer, was more than glad to make this conversion, since Ordnance was short a considerable number of 2 1/2-ton trucks, and had an overage of M-2 and M-3 halftracks. Changing the organization of 20 AW battalions to include 32 40's and 16 Wasps, utilized 320 surplus halftracks, and released 320 2 ½-ton trucks to other units that needed them desperately.

"The Wasps were employed as separate fire units, rather than as part of the 40mm sections. They proved to be capable companion pieces to the 40's, and in many cases were superior in both ground and AAA roles. Four 40's and two Wasps were assigned to each platoon.

"The other 16 M-51's taken from each of the 20 converted AW battalions were taken to Normandy with rear echelons and issued to gun battalions on the basis of 4 per battery in lieu of the four water-cooled machine guns. The M-51 could go any place a 90mm gun could go.

"As new AAA units joined First Army later in the operation, their first question usually was "When do we turn in our M-51's for M 16's?" Without exception, this increase in AW mobility and flexible fire power was welcomed at all echelons from the fire unit to Army Headquarters."

On the opposite side of the globe GIs were also modifying their half-tracks. Troops of the Coopers Plains Ordnance Depot on the south side of Brisbane, Australia succeeded in mounting 40mm Bofors guns on halftracks. The men of the 99th Ordnance Company removed the 37mm cannon and twin fifties from M15 Gun Motor Carriages, replacing them with the Bofors. Reportedly, 18 of these conversions were made and the resultant vehicles were issued to the 209th AAA Battalion. The vehicles found use on Luzon, primarily against ground targets. The dispersion of the fire encountered owing to the comparatively heavy recoil of the gun and the modest half-track suspension, which had caused Ordnance to reject a G-102-based half-track for anti-aircraft service, was of little concern against ground targets.

Interestingly, this would be a precursor to similar efforts a few years later.

Above: *When U.S. forces arrived in North Africa, M6 tank destroyers, like this one were among the vehicles landing. Soon it was found that the combination of a relatively small 37mm anti-tank gun and a wholly unarmored vehicle was inadequate for the task at hand. Reportedly over half of the M6s, also known by the Dodge model number WC-55 were lost. (Patton Museum)*

Below: *Shortly after Operation Torch, orders were issued to remove the 37mm guns from the bulk of the WC-55s, with the vehicles to be converted to standard WC-52 weapons carriers by means of a conversion kit. While the removed weapons were to be turned in, some units used them as ground mounts. Others however installed them on half-tracks. While still a poor tank destroyer, nevertheless the combination was potent against less formidable targets. (Chris Benedict collection)*

Above: When the Army began converting its 37mm Gun Motor Carriages M6 to weapons carriers by removing the 37mm Gun M3 mounts, some of these guns with their distinctive shields were installed on half-tracks. An example is "ROUGH RIDER II," of the 41st Armored Infantry Regiment, 2nd Armored Division, seen here during an exercise in England on 12 April 1944. (Chris Benedict collection)

Left: A 37mm Gun M3 mount in a half-track of the 41st Armored Infantry Regiment is seen from the rear in a 12 April 1944 photograph. The gun, its cradle, and the shield, which traversed in unison with the gun, are on a welded mount with a base plate that is bolted to I-beams on the floor. The gun is traversed toward the left. Several 37mm rounds in their packing tubes are to the far right. (Chris Benedict collection)

Right: *This 41st Infantry Regiment, 2nd Armored Division 81mm mortar carrier was photographed in England on 11 April 1944. Interestingly, the registration number W-4061237 S is identified by the Ordnance Department listing of Armored, Tank and Combat vehicles as being a M4A1 built on contract W-303-ORD-2078, yet in addition to having been part of the 41st program to remount the mortars to fire forward similar to the 81mm Mortar Carrier M21, the vehicle is equipped with a skate rail. (NARA)*

Left: *The fighting compartment of the modified 81mm Mortar Carrier M4A1 shown in the preceding photo is viewed from a closer perspective. The base plate of the mortar was in the very rear of the compartment. Open-topped ammunition bins were in the right rear of the fighting compartment and between the two built-in, closed-top ammo bins. Piggy-backed storage boxes were on the rear of the body. (Chris Benedict collection)*

Above: *The fighting compartment of the same modified 81mm Mortar Carrier M4A1, registration number W-4061237 S, is viewed from its rear end. Between the built-in, closed-top ammunition compartments at the front of the fighting compartment was an open bin for 16 mortar rounds. A radio set was on top of the right ammunition compartment. Note the curved track that supported the bipod of the mortar, and the M4 collimator sight on the left side of the mortar tube. (NARA)*

Below: *The crew of an 81mm Mortar Carrier M4 of the 3rd Infantry Division provide covering fire for advancing infantry near Werben, Germany, on 14 April 1945. This M4A1 was a conversion that the 3rd Infantry Division produced in which the ammunition compartments and doors were moved to the rear of the fighting compartment. Here, the left door is open, exposing the packing tubes inside. (NARA via Steve Zaloga)*

Above: *The crew of an 81mm mortar of Headquarters Company, 48th Armored Infantry Battalion, lay down fire against German troops near Overloon, Holland, on 6 October 1944. Based on the presence of the ammunition-compartment door to the rear of the cab, the vehicle appears to have been a Half-Track 81mm Mortar Carrier M4 with the mortar modified to fire to the front. A variety of gear is stowed about the vehicle: bedrolls, packs, a machine-gun tripod, a helmet and a carbine, and even a pair of muddy combat boots. Hand-painted mils or reference numbers have been applied to the front of the skate rail.* **Below:** *A column of half-tracks of the 3rd Armored Division pass through the newly liberated town of Theux, Belgium, on 10 September 1944. The closest vehicle appears to be a modified Half-Track 81mm Mortar Carrier M4; although no mortar is visible in the fighting compartment, mortar ammunition and their stowage bins are clearly present. Further, this vehicle is one of those that were converted in the field by reversing the side armor of the fighting compartment and relocating the covered ammunition compartments so that they and their external doors were to the rear of the vehicle instead of to the rear of the front doors. Note the bazooka stowed on the armored windshield. (NARA, both)*

Above: *In the Southwest Pacific, a number of Multiple Gun Motor Carriages M15s were converted by removing the 37mm and .50-caliber guns and mounts and substituting a 40mm Gun M1. These were nicknamed the "M15 Special." This example, registration number 4027007, was photographed at Finschhafen, Northeast New Guinea, on 9 November 1944. (Patton Museum)*

Left: *The gun mount of the M15 Special at Finschhafen is viewed from the front. The gun shield was cut out with a torch at the right front and the left front and side to accommodate the sights of the 40mm Gun M1. To the far left is a radio antenna base unit. (Patton Museum)*

Above: *The M51, Carriage Multiple Gun, consisted of M45 Quad mount installed in a low-slung, M17 tandem axle trailer. The trailers, produced by Fruehauf, J. G. Brill and Krieger Steel Sections, were based on a design that was created to transport searchlights and their associated generators. The low-slung design facilitated pushing the lights and generators, which had very small wheels, on and off the trailers.* **Below:** *The low loading height and long tongue of the trailers, however, limited the angle of approach and departure, and generally impeded the off-road mobility. This was a considerable restriction when utilized as a basis for the M51 antiaircraft weapon. This left the M51 better suited for dug-in positions such as this one in Germany in December 1944, than for more fluid battlefield uses. (NARA, both)*

Above: *Protecting a crossing of the Danube at Viehausen, Austria in April 1945, this 546th Antiaircraft Artillery; 65th Division, Third Army M51 exhibits the low ground clearance that hampered off-road mobility. This was one of the primary factors that led to the depot-level creation of the M16B "Wasp" by the First Army. (NARA)*

Below: *Quad .50-caliber machine guns on a Multiple Gun Motor Carriage M16B lay down fire in support of advancing infantry somewhere in Normandy on 12 July 1944. This vehicle can be identified as an M16B by the open access door to the rear of the right cab door, at the lower right of the photo. (Steve Zaloga collection)*

Above: The quad .50-caliber machine guns of a well-dug-in Half-Track Multiple Gun Motor Carriage M16B are firing at an aerial target while the G.I. to the rear of the turret observes the effect of the fire. Lying on the embankment in the foreground are five spare M2 ammunition chests. A stowage bin formed of lumber is on top of the cab. Evidence that the vehicle was a conversion from a Half-Track Car M2 is the area around the upper part of the fighting compartment, where the bolts holding the machine gun skate rail are located. (NARA)

Right: Two G.I.s are on alert for any signs of enemy aircraft in a Patterson conversion of M2 registration number 4024393-S, at Tuilleries gardens in Paris on 8 September 1944. This was during a period when Luftwaffe aircraft were attempting to conduct raids on the recently liberated city. Note the presence of one small storage box on the rear of the vehicle instead of the one small box and one large box found on the standard M16. (NARA)

Above: The nickname "Nazi Nemesis" is painted on the front of the shield of the quad .50-caliber machine gun turret on a half-track, possibly an M16B, of the 436th Antiaircraft Artillery Battalion (Automatic Weapons, Mobile) near St.-Denis, France, on 17 August 1944. The M16B was developed by Col. Charles G. Patterson of the U.S. First Army's Antiaircraft Artillery Section, mating quad .50-caliber machine gun turrets to Half-Track Cars M2. Thus, the M16B is sometimes called the "Patterson conversion." (Steve Zaloga collection) **Below:** A field-expedient multiple gun motor carriage formed by installing an M45 quad-.50-caliber machine gun turret on a Half-Track Car M2, assigned to the U.S. 35th Division, defends already damaged canal locks near Saareinsming, Alsace Lorraine, France, on 18 December 1944. A large rack on the rear of the vehicle holds liquid containers, packs, crates, and camouflage netting. (NARA)

Above: *A U.S. Seventh Army half-track with a Maxson machine gun turret trained to the rear guards against enemy aircraft attacks on a pontoon bridge over the Durance River in southern France on 25 August 1944. The camouflage netting and the angle of the gun mount preclude a precise identification of the vehicle type. (NARA via Steve Zaloga)*

Below: *U.S. troops pass by an Patterson-conversion Multiple Gun Motor Carriage M16B of the 456th Antiaircraft Artillery Battalion (Automatic Weapons, Mobile) that was knocked out during fighting in bocage country outside of St.-Lo in mid-July 1944. A stowage rack had been added to the rear of the vehicle. (Steve Zaloga collection)*

Above: *During a blizzard somewhere in western Germany on 8 February 1945, a crewman stands watch behind the quad machine gun mount on a Patterson-conversion Multiple Gun Motor Carriage M16B. A tarp has been draped over the turret to keep the snow off the gunner. A stowage rack is visible on the rear of the vehicle.* **Below:** *This rare photo of the interior of a M16B "Wasp"* shows the business end of a M45 Maxson quad .50-caliber machine-gun turret viewed close-up from the center of the cab. The skate rail was left in these vehicles, and on top of each side of the rail is a spare .50-caliber machine-gun barrel. The gunner is looking through a speed-ring sight. The cramped interior of the reconfigured M2 is apparent. (Steve Zaloga collection, both)

Two crewmen in a Half-Track Multiple Gun Motor Carriage M16B scan the sky, assisting the gunner to spot any approaching enemy aircraft. Boxed-up in the turret, with a clear view only to the front and above, the gunner relied on the other members of the crew to watch for threats in sectors of the sky that he was unable to see. (Steve Zaloga collection)

Chapter 6:
Field Use 1940-45

The Heavily Armed Half-Track at War

As the U.S. Army prepared for its seemingly inevitable entry into WWII, it was undergoing an aggressive campaign of modernization and mechanization. The M2 and M3 half-tracks, Standard Nomenclature List items G-102, were a part of this growth, and because they were in large-scale production by no less than three manufacturers, and proved automotively reliable, the chassis were quickly adapted to the variants detailed in this book.

As noted in the preceding chapters, oftentimes these variants were intended as expedients, pending later development—and sometimes simply the production of already-developed—of superior, fully-tracked motor carriages. The Japanese bombing of Pearl Harbor accelerated the already rapid pace of mechanization, from design to actual production.

Some of these improved vehicles came quickly off assembly lines, filling requirements of field units, and leading to the rapid withdrawal of the half-track—based motor carriages. As an example, the pilot of the M7 Priest, the T32, began testing in February 1942, was fully developed and coming off the assembly line in April. Quantity deliveries of the expedient T19, which was intended as a temporary substitute until the M7 could be fielded, began in February 1942 and ended in April, effectively gaining only two months over its successor.

The scenario of the T19 is not isolated, and goes a long way toward understanding the many instances where various specialized motor carriages were converted into more mundane personnel carriers, often without ever having been issued.

However, while there are many instances where half-track based expedient vehicles were superseded by their desired fully-tracked replacements, in some cases the desired replacements never materialized, and the G-102-based vehicles soldiered on until V-J Day. The M21 Mortar Carrier and the M15A1 and M16 Multiple Gun Motor Carriages are examples of vehicles whose planned successors failed to materialize until after World War II—in some cases years afterwards.

The Provisional Tank Group dispatched to the Philippines in November 1941 included half-tracks, which although criticized by officers there due to lack of overhead protection and thin armor, were nevertheless the best option available to them. Among the half-tracks used in the Philippines at that time was the 75mm gun motor carriage. Fifty of the vehicles were used to form three battalions of the Provisional Field Artillery Brigade, which were used in support of the Provisional Tank Group. After the fall of the Philippines, the Japanese placed some of these captured vehicles into service, using them against their former owners in 1944-45.

Elsewhere in the Pacific, the U.S. Marines employed the M3 Gun Motor Carriages, which they termed as Self Propelled Mounts, beginning in 1944 at Saipan. Unlike Europe, where the ever-increasing armor of German tanks proved the M3's 75mm gun gradually less effective, it remained an effective weapon against Japanese tanks, which were significantly

A 75mm Gun Motor Carriage T12 pauses on a grassy hillside during an exercise. The crewmen are wearing M1917 helmets, so the photo probably dates to the immediate prewar period or soon after the U.S. entry into World War II. (NARA)

less robust than those of their Axis ally. The Marines also used the vehicles for direct fire support.

As stated earlier in this volume, U.S. forces did not employ the T48 57mm Gun Motor Carriage. Russia was the primary user of this vehicle, designating it as the SU-57. The Soviets formed special independent tank destroyer brigades around these vehicles, assigning each brigade three battalions, each battalion comprised of 20 SU-57/T-48.

On the other side of the globe, Operation Torch saw five battalions of the M3 Gun Motor Carriage thrust into combat, owing to the slow delivery of the M10 tank destroyers. Regrettably, poorly informed decision-making brought about the vehicles being used for a variety of purposes they were neither intended, nor well-suited for. Concerning the 601st and 701st Tank Destroyer Battalions, the Army Ground Force reported: "....generally used in roles for which they were not designed such as infantry accompanying guns, assault artillery operating with tanks and in cordon defense instead of depth."

The exception to this generality was a single action by the 601st in March 1943 when the unit was instrumental in turning back an attack by the 10th Panzer Division near El Guetter. The 601st lost 21 of the M3 Gun Motor Carriages, but marked 30 of the Nazi tanks destroyed in the carnage.

Alongside the M3 Gun Motor Carriages in North Africa were the T30 75mm Howitzer Motor Carriages of the 1st Armored Division. Each of the Division's regiments received a dozen of the vehicles; three were assigned to the regimental reconnaissance battalions and three in each tank battalion headquarters platoon.

Nine T30s were also assigned to each of the 6th and 41st Armored Infantry Regiments, with three being assigned to the HQ platoon of each battalion. M8 Howitzer Motor Carriages gradually replaced the T30s, although some units utilized towed guns during a transition period.

Big brother to the T30 was the T19 105mm Howitzer Motor Carriage, commonly found in artillery battalions of armored infantry divisions and the cannon companies of infantry divisions. First deployed to North Africa, it was soon replaced by the M7 Priest.

One of the organizations using the T19 was the Cannon Company of the 16th Infantry Regiment, which was awarded the Presidential Unit Citation for its action against the Hermann Goering Panzer Division near Gela, Sicily on 10 July 1943.

Also joining in the action in North Africa was the T28E1 Multiple Gun Motor Carriage. Although justifiable criticized by the men serving on them due to the lack of armor protection for the gun crew, the men and their vehicles acquitted themselves well, being credited with 78 kills in a three-month span. Half of these kills came at Kasserine Pass, where the primary recipient of the wrath of the T28 were the vaunted Stukas, whose pilots mistook the tracer rounds of the .50-caliber machine guns as a sign of light armament, only to be greeted moments later by the powerful 37mm round—the AAA gunners having sighted in with the machine guns before firing the heavier weapon.

The M16 Multiple Gun Motor Carriage and the M15/M15A1 Multiple Gun Motor Carriages were assigned evenly, eight each, to the anti-aircraft artillery weapons company of each armored division in 1944. Infantry divisions, on the other hand, were initially assigned the M51 towed quad-fifty mounts, with AAA weapons battalions at the corps and army level having 32 each of the M15/M15A1 and M16 Multiple Gun Motor Carriages.

Despite their unit assignments, as well as the development process that created these vehicles, the work of the U.S. Army Air Force, and the air forces of the Allies, resulted in their being little anti-aircraft work to be done during the advance from Normandy and across Germany. There were, however, plenty of ground targets, and the withering firepower of the .50-caliber machine guns of both types, as well as the 37mm of the M15, was used with devastating effect against them.

The images on the following pages are arranged largely in chronological order, with occasional slight adjustments so to group the images by Theater. The photos presented were chosen to not only showcase the vehicles, but also the conditions under which that the troops operated them.

Above: *At a special demonstration of military equipment for members of Congress at Fort Belvoir, Virginia, on 2 October 1941, Vice President Henry A. Wallace peeps through the sight of the 75mm gun while Undersecretary of War Robert P. Patterson looks on. This vehicle had a twin .50-caliber machine gun mount to the rear of the 75mm gun. (NARA)*

Below: *During the U.S. Army's Carolinas Maneuvers on 20 November 1941 a pair of 75mm Gun Motor Carriages T12 of the "Blue Army" take up an overwatch position along a highway as civilian cars pass by. The vehicles and crews were assigned to the Provisional Tank Destroyer Battalion, 93rd Antitank Battalion, based at Fort Meade, Maryland. (NARA)*

Above: *Crewmen of the 93rd Antitank Battalion manning a 75mm Gun Motor Carriage T12 in a hull-down position along railroad tracks are on the lookout for approaching "enemy" tanks of the 69th Armored Regiment during the First Army's Carolina Maneuvers on 21 November 1941. The vehicle's U.S. Army registration number is visible: W-409545. (NARA)*

Below: *The same crew and 75mm GMC T12 shown in the preceding photograph are seen from a different perspective. The armored windshield has been lowered to give the 75mm gun freer play. The crew has stuck some tree branches on the vehicle for camouflage. (NARA)*

Above: *Within this T12, the section chief is standing in the right side of the cab with his left hand on the 75mm gun barrel, with several cannoneers behind him. A radio antenna and base unit are mounted above the front of the right door.* **Below:** *In an 81mm Mortar Carrier M4 during a prewar or early-war field exercise, the G.I. to the left is standing next to the mortar tube while the other one is aiming a Browning M1917 30-caliber water-cooled machine gun. The officer standing in the right door of the cab is not an American one but evidently an observer from a foreign army. (NARA, both)*

Above: *A close examination of this photo of a Half-Track 105mm Howitzer Motor Carriage T19 reveals that the crew members apparently are women, wearing U.S. Army tanker's helmets. The faded registration number on the hood is illegible. The .50-caliber antiaircraft machine gun to the rear of the howitzer has the early-type barrel support with elongated cooling slots.* **Below:** *The crew of a Half-Track 105mm Howitzer Motor Carriage T19 poses at their stations at a base* in Memphis, Tennessee. The vehicle's U.S. Army registration number was W-403610, placing it toward the latter part of production; a total of 324 of the T19s were produced. The bumper marking C 9 indicates that the half-track was assigned to a Battery C and was the 9th vehicle in the order of march. The nickname on the door, "Cathy," follows the Army tradition of nicknaming vehicles with the same first letter as the company or battery letter. (NARA, both)

Above: *A 75mm Gun Motor Carriage M3 based at Fort Custer, Michigan, is engaged in Army maneuvers at or near the base in August 1942. The V-shaped notch in the top of the armored windshield to accommodate the gun cradle in the travel position is clearly visible. (Patton Museum)* **Below:** *"AUTREY" is the nickname painted on the door of this Half-Track 75mm*

Howitzer Motor Carriage T30 at an open-house event at Fort McPherson, Georgia, on 9 April 1942. The shield was not installed on the howitzer mount. Autocar produced the two T30 pilots in early 1942, and the White Motor Company manufactured the 312 production T30s between February and April 1942. (Steve Zaloga collection)

Above: *Several U.S. Army half-tracks, including 75mm Gun Motor Carriage M3 U.S.A. number 4017140, are on display to the public in April 1942. The nickname "APACHE" is painted on the right door. The sign hanging from the side of the fighting compartment reads, "TANK DESTROYER COMPANY."*

Below: *Troops stand for inspection by their 75mm Gun Motor Carriages M3 at the Desert Training Center, Indio, California, on 31 May 1942. The event was the final inspection by General Pickering prior to his departure from the base. (NARA, both)*

Above: *The U.S. Army was segregated during most of World War II, and this 75mm Gun Motor Carriage M3 was manned by members of an unidentified African-American unit. The vehicle was photographed in the vicinity of Fort Custer, Michigan, in August 1943. Following the M3 are several 4x4 trucks armed with pedestal-mounted .50-caliber machine guns.* **Below:** *The*

Second Army conducted extensive maneuvers in Tennessee in the fall of 1942, during which time this 75mm Gun Motor Carriage M3 had to be towed by a wrecker to a maintenance base outside of Shelbyville. Note the rather ill-fitting cover on the 75mm gun barrel, cradle, and breech. (NARA, both)

A mortar crew practices firing in an 81mm Mortar Motor Carriage M4. The loader is about to drop the piece down the tube. To the right, the gunner has tilted his head away from the tube. To the rear is the section leader. Ready rounds packed in fiberboard tubes are in the bins to each side and in the left rear corner. (NARA)

Above: Members of Battery A, 59th Armored Field Artillery Battalion, stand for inspection at Camp Chaffee, Arkansas, on 31 October 1942. The first five half-tracks are 105mm Howitzer Motor Carriages T19. The contents of those vehicles' howitzer-section chests are laid out on the ground for inspection. Farther along the line are M3 and M2 half-tracks. (Patton Museum)

Below: Members of the crew of a Half-Track 105mm Howitzer Motor Carriage T19 practice loading a round into the piece during a field exercise on 31 October 1942. They were assigned to Battery B, 93rd Battalion, 6th Armored Field Artillery Group at Camp Chaffee, Arkansas. (Patton Museum)

Above: *The 105mm Howitzer M2A1 on a T19 has just been fired, and the spent casing is falling off the rear of the gun cradle during a field exercise of Battery C, 93rd Armored Field Artillery Battalion, at Camp Chaffee on 31 October 1942. The howitzer had a traverse of 20 degrees to either side of the longitudinal centerline of the vehicle. In the foreground is a pedestal-* *mounted 30-caliber antiaircraft machine gun.* **Below:** *During training at Camp Hood, Texas, members of a tank destroyer company pose on their dusty 75mm Gun Motor Carriages M3. The closest vehicle is registration number 4017502; this was from the initial production block of 1,350 M3s under contract W-670-ORD-1765. (Patton Museum, both)*

Above: *A column led by a Half-Track Car M2 followed by two 75mm Gun Motor Carriages M3 is driving along a British road on 28 October 1942. The section leaders are standing in the right sides of the cabs of the half-tracks. Note the lack of recognition stars on the vehicles at this point.* **Below:** *A 75mm Gun Motor Carriage M3 advances along a trail during a field exercise somewhere in England in October 1942. In the rear, a crewman is manning a .30-caliber machine gun, and he and the section leader, who is partially visible to the front of the shield, are wearing winter combat helmets, the lined hoods favored by armored troops. (Patton Museum, both)*

Above: *In a photo related to the preceding two, the crew of a 75mm GMC M3 practice setting up an antitank attack at an undisclosed location in England in 1942. All of the crewmen are wearing winter combat helmets. The section leader in the right front seat has the flaps of his helmet rolled up, and the driver is wearing goggles. (Patton Museum)*

Below: *Artillerymen practice firing the howitzer on a Half-Track Howitzer Motor Carriage T30 on a firing range at the Desert Training Center in California on 5 October 1942. A stowage rack fabricated from angle irons has been added to the right rear of the vehicle. "TOM TOM" is painted toward the bottom of the right door. (NARA)*

Above: *The crew of a Multiple Gun Motor Carriage T28E1 work to get their vehicle in order near Fedala Harbor, Morocco, on 8 November 1942, the first day of Operation Torch, the Allied invasion of French North Africa. Already they have cam- ouflaged the vehicle with brush. Although produced in small numbers, the T28E1 proved to be an excellent point-defense ve- hicle, guarding bridges, harbors, and bases against aerial attack.*

(NARA) **Below:** *A U.S. Army 75mm Howitzer Motor Carriage T30 is participating in an exercise or demonstration on a shore- line in or around November 1942. The name "FRANCES" has been painted roughly on the driver's door, and the identification star apparently has recently been painted on the side, as the overspray that extended past the stencil used for the star is visible. (Steve Zaloga collection)*

A 75mm Howitzer Motor Carriage T30 of the 143rd Infantry Regiment, 36th Infantry Division, is being hoisted from or lowered to a landing craft in November 1942. The 36th Division was nicknamed the Texas Division, and a map of that state is on the rear of the vehicle above the identification star. A roll of camouflage net is also on the rear of the half-track. A cover is installed over the howitzer breech. (NARA)

Personnel of an armored field artillery battalion load cased 105mm howitzer ammunition into an M3 half-track at Camp Chaffee, Arkansas, on 5 November 1942. The ammunition is in three-round "cloverleaf" bundles, constituting three fiberboard packing tubes with a clover-leaf-shaped cap on each end to hold the tubes together. (Patton Museum)

The crew of a Half-Track 105mm Howitzer Motor Carriage T19 attached to Battery C, 59th Armored Field Artillery Battalion, Camp Chaffee, Arkansas, on 9 November 1942. The typical crew of a T19 numbered six men, but up to eight men could be squeezed into the vehicle. A canvas cover has been installed over the gun and cradle. Marked on the left bumperette is a white circle; on the right bumperette is "C-29." Below the rear of the howitzer cradle is an M7 gun-section chest. (Patton Museum)

All eight crewmen are crammed into the same Half-Track 105mm Howitzer Motor Carriage T19 shown in the preceding photo. Their positions in the crew are painted on top of their helmets: "D" for driver and "CS" for chief of section in the cab, and "G" for gunner and cannoneers numbers 1 to 5 in the fighting compartment. (Patton Museum)

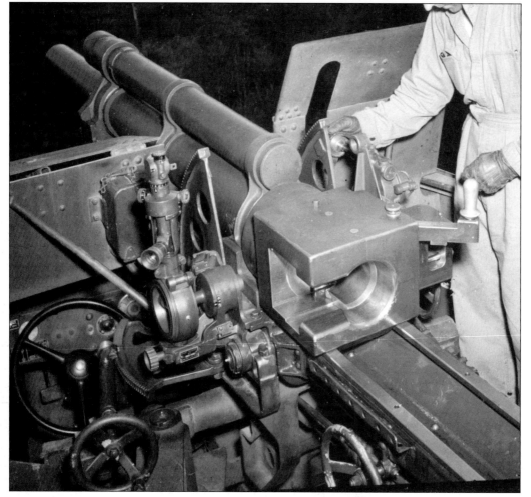

Above: *An M3 half-track personnel carrier being used as an ammunition carrier is loaded with cloverleaf packs of 105mm howitzer ammunition at Camp Chaffee, Arkansas, on 5 November 1942. The cloverleaf end caps that held the three packing tubes together were secured with a threaded rod and a wing nut. (Patton Museum)*

Left: *A sergeant is making an adjustment to the Range Quadrant M4 on the mount in a 105mm Howitzer Motor Carriage T19. The breech of the howitzer is in the open position. The flap on the left side of the howitzer shield is in the lowered position. To the far left, the steering wheel and instrument panel are visible. (NARA)*

Right: *The sergeant is inspecting the bore of the 105mm howitzer in the same T19. On the side of the howitzer cradle is the elevating hand wheel; the traversing hand wheel is farther forward. To the left front of the breech is the panoramic telescope on the Mount, Telescope, M21. Between the hand wheels is the left leg of the howitzer mount. (NARA)*

Below: *An artillery crew is training on a Half-Track 105mm Howitzer Motor Carriage T19 at a desert base in December 1942. Fabric covers are over the service headlights, which were the non-detachable type found on early-production vehicles. These headlights proved susceptible to blast damage from the howitzer. "A 18" is marked on the left side of the bumper, the A signifying the company letter and the 18 indicating this vehicle's number in the order of march. (NARA)*

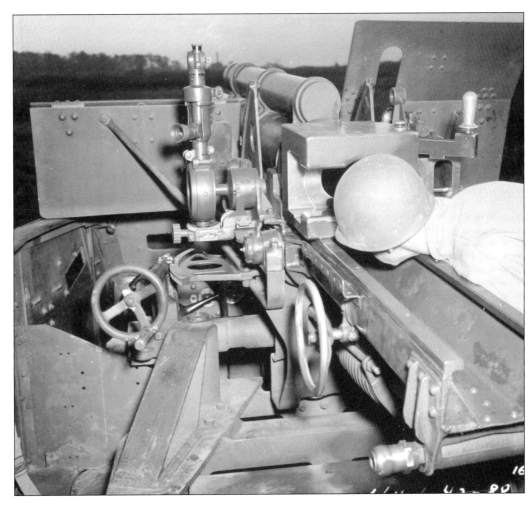

Above: *This photo of a Half-Track 105mm Howitzer Motor Carriage T19 may have been taken at the same locale and time-frame as the preceding photo, but the vehicle is different, having the number 13 on the bumper for its order of march. Separate dust covers are on the muzzle of the howitzer and the barrel, cradle, and recoil cylinder.* **Below:** *Six Half-Track 105mm Howitzer* *Motor Carriages T19 are lined up at the Desert Training Center, Indio, California, in December 1942. On the nearest vehicle, the identification star is on a square-shaped patch of paint that is lighter than the paint on the rest of the side of the vehicle. On the second vehicle, note the small cover over the front of the recuperator cylinder over the howitzer barrel. (NARA, both)*

H301

Above: *At the same facility depicted in the preceding photograph a 75mm Gun Motor Carriage is viewed from the front. The forward part of the gun barrel and cradle are of a signifi cantly darker color than the Olive Drab on the remainder of the vehicle, perhaps an attempt at camouflaging the gun. An M7 Priest self-propelled 105mm howitzer is in the right background.*

Below: *During World War II the U.S. Marine Corps was equipped with several hundred 75mm Gun Motor Carriages M3, such as these four at an undisclosed base. The Marines had their own system of vehicle registration numbers; the first two M3s are U.S.M.C. 61655 and 61656. (NARA, both)*

Above: *The same line of U.S.M.C. 75mm Gun Motor Carriages M3 in the preceding photo is seen from a different angle, with U.S.M.C. 61655 and 61656 in the foreground. There are at least 12 75mm GMCs M3 in the row. Storage boxes were on the rears of the bodies: this was not a standard feature on Army M3s.* **Below:** *During training exercises in the South Pacific in 1942, the 75mm gun of a U.S. Marine Corps M3 gun motor carriage has just been fired. Sections of a rammer staff are secured with straps to the top of the body on either side of the fighting compartment. The 75mm gun generated considerable blast to the front of the vehicle. (NARA, both)*

Above: *The crew of a camouflage-painted Combination Gun Motor Carriage T28EI of the 477th Antiaircraft Artillery Battalion search the sky for signs of enemy aircraft in North Africa on 24 February 1943. All but two of the 80 T28EIs produced were assigned to the 477th. It's not clear if the camouflage treatment applied over the Olive Drab base color was mud or paint. (NARA)* **Below:** *A Half-Track 75mm Howitzer Motor Carriage T30 is being lowered over the side of U.S.S. Leonard Wood (AP-25) onto an LCM-3 off Solomons Island on 3 March 1943. The 75mm howitzer barrel and cradle are enclosed in a fabric cover. Note the sag of the track and the bogie wheel assemblies when the vehicle was hoisted. (Steve Zaloga collection)*

Above: *A column of U.S. Army 75mm Gun Motor Carriages M3 is stopped along a North African highway on 4 March 1943 so the crewmen can grab a quick snack. All of the 75mm guns have their dust covers on: evidence that these forces were not in a combat zone. (U.S. Army Quartermaster Museum)* **Below:** *Officers of the 601st Tank Destroyer Battalion pore over a map in front of an M2 half-track while a 75mm Gun Motor Carriage M3 is positioned behind an embankment in the background. The scene was during the Battle of El Guettar, Tunisia, a slugging match between Lt. Gen. George S. Patton's II Corps and Gen. von Arnim's Army Group Africa on 23 March 1943. (Patton Museum)*

A U.S.M.C. 75mm Gun Motor Carriage M3 is being lowered from a transport ship to a landing craft somewhere in the South Pacific on 4 May 1943. The driver is at the wheel, ready to advance as soon as the landing craft lowers the ramp at the shore. A cover is fitted over the 75mm gun, and a tarpaulin is secured over the fighting compartment. (U.S.M.C.)

Above: *Crewmen of a U.S.M.C. 75mm GMC M3 wash their vehicle in preparation for a parade on an island in the South Pacific during July 1943. A close inspection of the photo reveals that the vehicle was painted in a camouflage scheme mimicking jungle vegetation, apparently consisting of lighter-colored daubs of paint over the Olive Drab base color.* **Below:** *A U.S.M.C. 75mm GMC M3, left, and several 4x4 trucks with pylon-mounted .50-caliber machine guns pointing skyward are part of a group of vehicles parked near Tetere Beach, Guadalcanal. The hoods of the vehicles are popped open, perhaps for inspection. On the M3, a radio antenna is mounted on a flat, angled plate that is casting a long shadow on the side of the cab. (U.S.M.C., both)*

Above: *A Combination Gun Motor Carriage T28E1, distinguished by the two water-cooled .50-caliber machine guns located above the 37mm gun, is being backed up the ramp of a landing Craft, Tank (LCT) in preparation for the July 1943 invasion of Sicily. A reel of wire is stored on top of the windshield, and two five-gallon liquid containers are on holders to the front of the cab.* **Below:** *In a field outside of Licata, Sicily, three* camouflage-painted Half-Track 75mm Howitzer Motor Carriages T30 are being readied to fire in support of infantry that are landing nearby, on 10 July 1943. Note the irregularly applied and non-uniform recognition stars on the half-tracks to the left and the center; the stars are tilted in different directions, and the circles surrounding them are of different thicknesses. (Steve Zaloga collection, both)*

Above: *The three Half-Track 75mm Howitzer Motor Carriages T30 as the preceding photo. Visible on the sides of the fighting compartments of the first two vehicles are unit markings called ETOUSA POM (ETO U.S. Army Preparation for Overseas Movement) Unit Serial Numbers. They were issued to every sub-unit within a division before major amphibious operations, and in the Mediterranean Theater, the typical format was a four-digit number followed by a letter, along with horizontal bars and the same letter. The code on the nearest vehicle is 2651-R. The three bars were color-coded to the last two digits of the number, with the middle stripe representing the last digit and the top and bottom stripes representing the next to last digit. (Steve Zaloga collection)*

Right: *The nickname "CUNNING-HAM" is painted on the driver's door of this Half-Track 75mm Howitzer Motor Carriage assigned to Company C, 82nd Reconnaissance Battalion, 2nd Armored Division. It was photographed during the advance through Rebera, Sicily, on 25 July 1943. The hinged panel at the lower front of the howitzer shield is in the open position; note the latch that held it in the raised position. (Steve Zaloga collection)*

Above: On a hillside road in Sicily in the summer of 1943, a Half-Track 75mm Howitzer Motor Carriage T30 has paused to fire at a German artillery position. Painted on the side of the fighting compartment are, from front to rear, a U.S. flag; a faded, possibly painted-over recognition star; and an upside-down recognition star within a circle. Two rear-facing .30-caliber machine guns and one forward-facing .50-caliber machine gun are mounted on the vehicle. (Steve Zaloga collection)

Left: A Half-Track 75mm Howitzer Motor Carriage T30 rolls down a war-torn street in Sicily in the summer of 1943. The identification star has been painted upside down. Visible to the right are a .50-caliber machine gun and a 30-caliber machine gun. Note the unit code, a letter R and horizontal bars, on the side and rear of the fighting compartment. (Steve Zaloga collection)

Above: *During the invasion of Sicily around 1 August 1943 a U.S. Army 75mm Gun Motor Carriage M3 squeezes through a very narrow passageway in Cerami. Markings on the rear of the vehicle identify it as assigned to the Antitank Company of the 39th Infantry Regiment, 9th Infantry Division.* **Below:** *Two Marines perform maintenance on the gun of a 75mm GMC M3 on New Guinea on 17 October 1942. On the frame above the right door is an unusual antenna mount consisting of a round plate on top of a rearward-tilted box-shaped base. On the cowl is a small marking for a Special Weapons Battalion. (Patton Museum, both)*

Above: *Marines maneuver their 75mm GMC M3s into position for a regimental parade while training in Australia. This photo was taken on 29 July, 1943. All the crews wear the popular "garrison" cap and are dressed rather uncharacteristically for chilly weather. (NARA)* **Below:** *A U.S. Marine Corps 75mm Gun Motor Carriage M3 lands on a thin shoreline at Cape*

Gloucester, New Britain, during the battle that began in late December 1943 and extended until April of the following year. The vehicle had a three-color camouflage paint scheme, and a Browning .30-caliber machine gun is mounted on the right side of the fighting compartment. An insignia is on the side of the body. (U.S.M.C.)

Above: *Marines advance through a thicket on New Gloucester, accompanying a 75mm Gun Motor Carriage M3. Chains are installed on the tires to assist with traction, and those on the right tire are visible. The half-track is rigged with tree branches for camouflage purposes. (U.S.M.C.)* **Below:** *Some of the Combination Gun Motor Carriages T28EI that* served in North Africa later made their way across the Mediterranean to Italy, where they continued to provide excellent protection against low-flying enemy aircraft. This example serving with Battery A, 443rd Antiaircraft Battalion, in the Venafro sector on 19 November 1943 exhibits kill markings for six aircraft on the storage chest to the rear of the cab. (NARA)

Above: Members of the 434th Coast Artillery Battalion pose with their Half-Track Combination Gun Motor Carriage M15A1 at a site in the Capua sector in Italy on 20 November 1944. On the ground is 1st Lt. L.H. Thompson, and on the gun platform are, left to right, Pfc. Divio Hernandez, Cpl. Frank Gonzalez, and Pvt. Dan Ramirez. Note the antenna and its mounting bracket on the cowl of the half-track. **Below:** A Marine M2 half-track with a 75mm gun and shield of the type used on the 75mm

GMC M3 rolls down the ramp of a landing ship, tank (LST) on Cape Gloucester, New Britain, on D-day, 26 December 1943. The vehicle was a virtual fortress, with a .30-caliber machine gun to the front of the front right seat and two .50-caliber machine guns with M2 ammunition chests in the fighting compartment. A radio antenna is on an unusual bracket over the left side of the windshield frame. (NARA, both)

Above: *In another photo of U.S.M.C. landings on New Britain, a 75mm GMC M3 disembarks from a landing craft. The number 75911 is marked on the bumper and the side of the hood; it may have been a U.S.M.C. registration number. Also on the bumper and toward the front of the side of the hood is the diamond-shaped symbol of the 1st Marine Division. A small pedestal mount for a machine gun is on the right side of the hood.* **Below:** *A Marine 75mm GMC M3 splashes ashore from LST-202 at Cape Gloucester. The vehicle appears to have been painted overall in Olive Drab, but there is a light color on the front of the gun's slide bearing at the front of the cradle. This may have been tape or protective material to protect the slide bearing from corrosion. (U.S.M.C., both)*

The Japanese captured a number of U.S. 75mm Gun Motor Carriages T12 in the Philippines in 1942. An American photographer snapped this image of one of those T12s, in Japanese markings, where it fell into a river during the U.S. advance in the Philippines in the final months of the war. (U.S.M.C.)

Above: *A vivid camouflage pattern has been applied to this Half-Track Multiple Gun Motor Carriage M15 at an unidentified location in 1943. Although the guns are covered, the shapes of two .50-caliber machine gun barrels are discernible above the barrel of the 37mm automatic gun. This vehicle and the multiple gun motor carriage to the right (presumably also an M15) have vertical tail pipes by the engine compartments: likely part of a deep-fording kit.* **Below:** *A Half-Track 75mm Howitzer Motor Carriage T30, registration number 4016025, is being employed in a winter training exercise. The shield on the howitzer mount is the revised model with a reduced height. The handle on the top front of the howitzer cradle provides a handhold for the man standing in the cab, dressed in a tanker's helmet and jacket and holding a Thompson submachine gun. (Jim Gilmore collection, both)*

Above: *A Half-Track Multiple Gun Motor Carriage M15 rests at a desert base sometime during 1943. The first six digits of the vehicle's registration number are faintly visible on the side of the hood: 408351. The cab and the gun mount are equipped with canvas tops.* **Below:** *In a photograph related to the preceding and the following ones, vehicles as a desert base include a Half-Track Multiple Gun Motor Carriage M15 to the right of center. A close examination of the photo reveals that the arrangement of the guns hidden by the cover on the gun mount is two .50-caliber machine guns over a 37mm automatic gun, indicative of an M15. (Air Defense Artillery Museum, both)*

Above: *A half-track multiple gun motor carriage, likely an M15, is at the center of the photograph. In addition to the canvas top attached to the shield of the gun mount, a smaller cover is over the gun barrels. (Air Defense Artillery Museum)* **Below:** *Marines manning a 75mm GMC M3 are vigilant for the approach of the enemy at the airfield at Cape Gloucester, New* *Britain, in January 1944. On the cowl of the half-track is a U.S.M.C. unit symbol consisting of a square representing 1st Marine Division, with "SW" inside it, indicating "Special Weapons Battalion," the number 1 to the left, and the letter D to the bottom. All of this indicated Battery D, 1st Special Weapons Battalion, 1st Marine Division. (Patton Museum)*

Above: Two members of the crew of a Multiple Gun Motor Carriage M15 of the 105th Antiaircraft Artillery Battalion scan the sky through binoculars for enemy aircraft at a hilltop location in the San Pietro area of Italy on 3 January 1944. Camouflage netting has been erected to mask the vehicle, whose headlights are faintly visible to each side of the G.I. in the foreground. (U.S.M.C.) **Below:** A Half-Track Multiple Gun Motor Carriage M15 is positioned to defend a hilltop area near San Pietro, Italy, on 8 January 1944. The vehicle was assigned to Battery D, 105th Antiaircraft Artillery Battalion. A camouflage-paint pattern is discernible on the door of the cab, and an unusual camouflage net covered with light-colored (and probably artificial) sprigs is tightly stretched over the armored shield. (NARA)

Above: *Members of Battery C, 441st Antiaircraft Artillery Battalion, man a twin .50-caliber machine gun mount on a half-track well-concealed by camouflage netting near Anzio on 26 January 1944. Although details of the half-track are sparse, it is assumed that this was a Multiple Gun Motor Carriage M13 judging by the twin .50-caliber machine-gun mount. (Steve Zaloga collection)* **Below:** *On a battlefield in the southern Pacific on 26 February 1944, personnel of a 75mm Gun Motor Carriage M3 take a break in the action. A camouflage-paint pattern is discernible on the cab door. At the rear of the half-track is an interesting pedestal mount for a .30-caliber machine gun, fabricated from plumbing materials: sections of pipe and elbows. (U.S.M.C.)*

Above: *A U.S.M.C. 75mm Gun Motor Carriage M3 advances along a road on Roi-Namur during the Battle of Kwajalein in early 1944. A machine-gun tripod is lashed to the rear door. Faintly visible on the lid of the ammo box of the .50-caliber machine gun is the Unit Numerical Identification System (UNIS) symbol for Weapons Company, 4th Marines: the number 402 inside a semicircle. (U.S.M.C.)*

Below: *Smoke and dust obscure a 75mm Gun Motor Carriage of the 24th Marine Regiment as it advances on Roi-Namur on 2 February 1944. The shape faintly visible on the side of the body below the gun shield is the likeness of a Vargas pinup girl in a recumbent position. Note the crate and the miscellaneous gear on the front of the vehicle above the anti-ditching roller. (U.S.M.C.)*

Above: *A crewman mounts a camouflage-painted Half-Track 75mm Howitzer Motor Carriage T30 while two others prepare to put the howitzer into action at Anzio, Italy, on 8 March 1944. The men and the vehicle were assigned to the Cannon Company, 179th Infantry. Painted on the side of the fighting compartment is the nickname "HAIRBRETH [sic] HARRY" (Patton Museum)* **Below:** *The tracks and tires of a Combination Gun Motor Carriage M15A1 of the 474th*

Antiaircraft Artillery Battalion have sunk deep in the sand during pre-D-day rehearsal landings at Slapton Sands, England, on 27 April 1944. The M15A1 had a combat-loaded weight of approximately 20,000 pounds, and this vehicle clearly was overloaded, with crates stowed on the bumper, a slatted rack to the rear of the fender holding tire chains and boxes, and a wooden box above the windshield holding ammunition boxes and other gear. (NARA)

Above: *In a scene of U.S. Army vehicles being loaded aboard landing craft at a port in England in preparation for the D-day landings in Normandy, there is little to identify the type of this half-track aside from the glimpse of a gun tub to the rear of the cab. This evidently was a Half-Track Combination Gun Motor Carriage M15A1, armed with a 37mm gun and twin .50-caliber machine guns on a common mount. (NARA)* **Below:** *During the Battle of Saipan in June 1944, a 75mm Gun Motor Carriage M3 fires at a Japanese strongpoint near Garapan. A dark-colored camouflage pattern is visible on the side of the gun shield and on the cab and body. The crew's knapsacks and packs are strapped to the side of the fighting compartment. (U.S.M.C.)*

Above: *The 75mm gun of a Marine M3 gun motor carriage is in full recoil during a fire mission against a Japanese position on the road to ChaCha, Saipan, on 25 June 1944. Two .30-caliber machine guns are on pintle mounts on the sides of the fighting compartment. (U.S.M.C.)*

Right: *For heavier firepower than Browning .30-caliber machine guns could offer, this 75mm Gun Motor Carriage M3 of the 4th Marine Division on Saipan in June 1944 was armed with two Browning .50-caliber M2 HB machine guns on heavy-duty pedestal mounts. An unusual holder for boxes has been installed on the right side of the rear of the vehicle, and a rail has been placed on the side of the fighting compartment to hold packs. (Patton Museum)*

Left: A U.S.M.C. 75mm GMC M3 advances along a trail in the southern Pacific area. Faintly discernible on the right side of the fender is the semicircular UNIS symbol of the 4th Marine Division. The half-track is armed with two .50-caliber machine guns, barrels pointed upward, in addition to the 75mm main gun. (U.S.M.C.)

Below: A group of Marines gathered on and around a 75mm GMC M3 with the letter A on the front of the gun shield observe the fighting on the plain below at Makunsha, Saipan. In addition to two .30-caliber machine guns in the rear of the vehicle, there is a less obvious .30-caliber machine gun to the front of the Marine sitting in the right side of the cab. This gun is fed by the belt of ammo draped over the barrel of the 75mm gun. (U.S.M.C.)

Above: *This U.S.M.C. 75mm Gun Motor Carriage M3 was knocked out during combat in the Marianas in 1944. Sources vary on whether it was photographed on Saipan on 16 June or later on Tinian. Numerous bullet holes are in evidence on the vehicle and the gun shield, and the right track was blown off. A bazooka is stowed behind the front tow hooks, and "6M" is painted on the right side of the front bumper. (NARA)*

Right: *Among a litter of discarded 75mm ammunition packing tubes, a U.S.M.C. 75mm GMC M3 slams away at a Japanese stronghold on Tinian on 30 July 1944. Attached to the rear-pointing .30-caliber gun on the right side of the fighting compartment is a finger-jointed wood ammunition box. The crew's packs are strapped to the side of the vehicle, and storage boxes, crates, and an oil drum are secured to the rear of the half-track. (NARA)*

Above: *A 75mm Gun Motor Carriage M3 with its main gun depressed supports Marine infantry during fighting on Saipan in July 1944. A close inspection of the photo shows that a camouflage paint scheme was present on the vehicle, with a faint pattern detectable on the side of the body and a more pronounced pattern on the side of the gun shield.* **Below:** *Several Marines to the right observe as a 75mm Gun Motor Carriage M3 fires* *on Japanese troops on Saipan in the summer of 1944. Crew packs and gear are stowed on the rear of the fighting compartment. Alongside the body to the rear of the cab is what appears to have been a temporary, makeshift tail pipe, although the outlet of the stock tail pipe is visible to the lower front of the track-support rollers. (U.S.M.C., both)*

Above: *A bulky dust cover is over the main gun of this camouflage-painted 75mm GMC M3 proceeding alongside a group of infantrymen somewhere in the southern Pacific. On the left side of the half-track's fender and on the side of the hood is the number 4018133, while on the opposite side of the bumper and repeated on the hood is the UNIS symbol for the 1st Marine Division. Netting is stretched over the gun shield, probably for purposes of attaching branches and foliage for camouflage.*

(US Army Engineer School History Office) **Below:** *A Marine 75mm GMC M3 has been blasting at point-blank range some sandbagged Japanese bunkers on the hillside directly to the front. The photo is assumed to have been taken on Saipan in the summer of 1944. The M3 is painted in a three-color camouflage scheme. Note the holstered rifle or carbine to the front of the driver's door. (U.S.M.C.)*

An amtrack, right, approaches a U.S.M.C. 75mm Gun Motor Carriage M3 on Saipan around July 1944. The right side of the M3's hood is partially open, perhaps for some quick maintenance or to allow the engine to cool. (U.S.M.C.)

Above: *On Saipan in the summer of 1944, a Marine 75mm GMC M3 advances down a road. A three-color camouflage paint scheme is present on the vehicle but is very subtle in this photo. Stacked above the top rear of the fighting compartment are fiberboard packing tubes for 75mm ammunition. Dust covers are over the .machine guns of the fighting compartment.*

Below: *Two 75mm Gun Motor Carriages M3 pass by a roadside ammunition dump somewhere in the Pacific in the summer of 1944. On the first vehicle, a skyward-pointing .50-caliber machine gun is on a pintle mount to the rear of the gun shield. The number 1411 is stenciled on the left side of the bumper. (U.S.M.C, both.)*

Above: *A Marine crouching next to a 75mm GMC M3 observes the effect of the fire as the main gun blasts a Japanese position in the distance. The armored windshield is in the raised position but the driver's sliding visor is open. Note the section of rammer staff secured to the top of the side armor of the fighting compartment.* **Below:** *Marines in a 75mm GMC M3 take* advantage of a lull in the action to relax and prepare for the next round of fighting on Suipan. The rearmost man in the vehicle has the barrel of a dismounted 30-caliber machine gun in his left hand. Next to it is another, mounted, 30-caliber machine gun and ammo box. (U.S.M.C., both)

Above: *A wrecked 75mm GMC M3 with the letter D on the gun shield lies along a trail. The photo is thought to have been taken on Tinian around July 1944. A number painted on the right side of the bumper is partially legible, starting with 40181. The early-style headlights are dismounted; these often were taken off because the blast of the 75mm gun damaged them. (U.S.M.C.)* **Below:** *Quantities of 75mm GMCs M3 were* transferred to the British in the field. The Brits tended to use these vehicles for fire support instead of as tank destroyers. These M3s of the King's Dragoon Guards, 23rd Armoured Brigade, are deployed as mobile field artillery in the vicinity of Monte Cairo, near Cassino, Italy, on 20 February 1944. On the cradle of the nearest 75mm gun is painted the nickname "BELCHING BELLA." (NARA)*

Above: *Outside of a picturesque town in southern France in August 1944, a 105mm Howitzer Motor Carriage T19 is shelling a German strongpoint. Faintly visible through the camouflage netting rigged over the vehicle is a large recognition star with a circle around it, on the side of the body. In the center background is a towed 105mm howitzer under camouflage netting. (U.S.M.C.)* **Below:** *Crewmen of a Half-Track Combination Gun Motor Carriage M15A1 fraternize with French civilians at the old chateau at Château-Thierry, France, on 31 August 1944. The guns had a commanding position overlooking the Marne River valley. The canvas rear curtain is installed on the shield of the gun mount. A stowage bin with a rear-tilted backside is on top of the raised armored windshield. (NARA)*

Above: *Members of a U.S.M.C. 75mm GMC M3 crew greet a column of infantrymen crossing a field on Guam during the U.S. liberation of that island in 1944. No visible markings are on the vehicle. Tire chains are installed, and a tow chain is wrapped around the tow hooks on the bumper. (U.S.M.C.)* **Below:** *Members of the 443rd Antiaircraft Artillery Battalion man a* Combination Gun Motor Carriage T28E1 *at the St.-Rafael airfield in southern France on 17 August 1944. This vehicle was a veteran of fighting in North Africa and Italy. Note the cooling-water supply hoses attached to the machine guns, and the two pictures of pinup girls pasted to the inside of the driver's door. (Steve Zaloga collection)*

Above: *A Marine 75mm GMC M3 is on the advance on Peleliu in September 1944. On the rear and the side of the body are semicircular markings with the letter W in the center. In addition to a .30-caliber machine gun, the vehicle carries a .50-caliber machine gun in the rear end with a dust cover over it. On a rack on the left rear of the body are two M2 ammunition chests* for the .50-caliber machine gun. **Below:** *A Marine 75mm GMC M3, either the same one in the preceding photo or one from the same unit, pounds away at Japanese forces during the hellish combat on Peleliu in September 1944. Visible above the shoulders of the Marine with the M1 carbine in the foreground is an M2 ammunition chest. (U.S.M.C, both.)*

Above: *Corporals John McLaughlin, left, and Oliver St. Dennis stand guard on a Combination Gun Motor Carriage M15A1 outside of Hoeville, France, on 3 November 1944. The hinged frontal armor flaps of the gun shield are lowered, and on the side of the shield is a recognition star and a round insignia or marking. Note the camouflage netting on the chassis at the bottom.* **Below:** *Although at first glance the vehicle to the left would seem to be a* Half-Track Multiple Gun Motor Carriage M16, a close look reveals that the chassis is not the M3-type half-track the M16 was based upon but an M2. This GMC and the 40mm Bofors gun to the right were firing at ground targets in Germany on 2 November 1944. Four liquid containers are on a rack on the side of the half-track, and a large stowage box or bin with a canvas cover on the sides is on the rear. (NARA, both)*

Above: *Considering the several wrecked vehicles, including the half-track multiple gun motor carriage with its guns stripped off to the left, in bombed-out Bastogne, Belgium, on 30 December 1944, the sign to the right seethes with irony: "Unattended vehicles will be impounded by military police." (NARA)* **Below:** *Crewmen of a Half-Track Multiple Gun Motor Carriage M16 of* the 489th Antiaircraft Artillery Battalion, Third Army, watch a formation of C-47 cargo planes (far left) as they approach Bastogne to air-drop supplies on 27 December 1944. Several foxholes have been excavated next to the half-track: temporary homes for the crewmen during the long winter nights and frequent shellings and bombings. (NARA)

Above: *A Half-Track Combination Gun Motor Carriage MI5AI guards a bridge over the Meuse River in Sedan, France, in December 1944. The vehicle was assigned to Battery D, 467th Antiaircraft Artillery Battalion. A faint design, possibly in chalk, on the side of the body of the half-track appears to be a representation of a rampant lion. (NARA)*

Below: *Members of the 778th Antiaircraft Artillery Battalion, 3rd Armored Division, man a snow-caked Combination Gun Motor Carriage MI5AI near Bastogne, Belgium, on 19 January 1945. The crewmen are, left to right, Pfc. Kenneth Duncan, Tech. 5 John B. Lee, Pvt. H. J. McMullen, and Tech. 5 Howard Freeman. (Patton Museum)*

Above: An "M15 Special" field-expedient 40mm gun mount on an M3 half-track, similar to the one seen earlier in two November 1944 photographs from Finschhafen, Northeast New Guinea, pummels Japanese troops along the Yamashita Line near San Nicolas, Luzon, Philippine Islands, on 9 April 1945. The crew and vehicle were assigned to the 209th Antiaircraft Artillery Battalion, and this was the first time this type of weapon had been used against enemy ground troops in this area. Vehicles of this type were converted at the Coopers Plains 99th Ordnance Depot in Australia. (NARA)

Left: Crewmen of a half-track assigned to the 376th Antiaircraft Artillery Battalion dig out their snowbound vehicle near Monschau, Germany, on 20 January 1945. The vehicle appears to be a Half-Track Multiple Gun Motor Carriage M16, with the distinctive quad-.50-caliber gun mount cover installed over the Maxson turret. Note the humps at the upper corners of the cover where it encloses the M2 ammunition chests. (NARA)

Above: *On a landing beach on Iwo Jima in February 1945, a disabled U.S.M.C. 75mm Gun Motor Carriage M3 sits axle-deep in the sand. The vehicle, including the 75mm gun barrel and shield, was painted in a camouflage scheme consisting of at least four colors. The lightest color is visible on top of the gun shield. Chains are present on the partially buried tire.* **Below:** *"TARHEEL" was the nickname of this 75mm GMC M4, seen on*

Iwo Jima on 25 February 1945. On the right side of the bumper is the UNIS symbol for Weapons Company, 28th Marine Regiment, 5th Marine Division. The number 71075 is painted on the left side of the bumper. Note the bullet hole in the roller, the bent left fender, and the sandbags on the hood. A camouflage pattern with straight, diagonal borders is visible on the gun shield. (U.S.M.C., both)

Left: *A member of Battery B, 571st Antiaircraft Artillery Battalion, stands by with a 10-round ammo clip for the 37mm Gun M1A2 of a Combination Gun Motor Carriage M15A1 in the Kornelimünster sector in Germany 3 January 1945. Another clip of ammunition is already inserted in the gun. To the right, another crewman makes an adjustment to the right .50-caliber machine gun. (NARA)*

Below: *A Maxson quad-.50-caliber machine gun and the half-track it formerly was mounted in are in ruins after the vehicle ran over a land mine on Iwo Jima in February 1945. Scattered on the ground are ammunition boxes and belts, tools, a canteen, and other contents of the half-track. To the right is the rear of the body. (NARA)*

Right: *When the U.S. Army captured the Ludendorff Bridge on the Rhine River at Remagen, Germany, on March 7, 1945, the defense of this strategically important crossing from German air attack became of paramount importance. This was a task in which the Half-Track Combination Gun Motor Carriage M15A1 excelled. An example is emplaced on a railroad track with the Ludendorff Bridge in the background, on 17 March, shortly before the bridge collapsed. Next to it is a Half-Track Multiple Gun Motor Carriage M16. (Air Defense Artillery Museum)*

Below: *A Multiple Gun Motor Carriage M16 is positioned to defend the Ludendorff Bridge at Remagen, Germany, against German air attack following the 7 March 1945 U.S. capture of the bridge. The crew has made an effort to camouflage the vehicle with tarps and miscellaneous objects, such as the wheelbarrow by the front of the half-track. Another Multiple GMC M16 is to the left front of this half-track. (Steve Zaloga collection)*

During the defense of the bridgehead at Remagen, Germany, a Half-Track Multiple Gun Motor Carriage M16 is emplaced on railroad tracks along the Rhine River. A large box for equipment and supplies is on the rear of the fighting compartment. Partially hidden to the right of the half-track is a trailer full of gear. (Air Defense Artillery Museum)

Above: *In a companion view to a preceding image, the same two Multiple Gun Motor Carriages M16 are seen from a different angle as they provide antiaircraft protection for the Ludendorff Bridge in early March 1945. The tarps and the objects piled up against the vehicles would make them less readily distinguishable to enemy gunners and attacking pilots. (Steve Zaloga*

collection) **Below:** *A half-track with a quad-.50-caliber Maxson turret, apparently a Multiple GMC M16, is emplaced along the Rhine River around Remagen, Germany, ready to take on any attacking German planes. The rear of the fighting compartment is toward the camera. Baggage boxes and tarpaulins are piled up on and next to the vehicle. (Air Defense Artillery Museum)*

Above: *Crewmen of an antiaircraft battery unit take a break around a Half-Track Combination Gun Motor Carriage M15A1 during the defense of the bridgehead at Remagen. The rear of the half-track is in the foreground, and the gun mount is traversed to the right to cover approaches over the Rhine River. To the left are boxes of 37mm ammunition; a 10-round clip is sitting on top of one of the boxes. **Below:** In the foreground, along the west bank of the Rhine River on the west side of* Remagen, a Half-Track Combination Gun Motor Carriage M15A1 stands watch, its guns pointed over the river. The mountain faintly visible in the distance is the Erpler Ley, the mountain on the east shore overlooking Remagen. Also, very faintly visible is the Ludendorff Bridge, which was still standing when this photo was taken; it would collapse on 17 March. (Air Defense Artillery Museum, both)

Above: A Half-Track Combination GMC M15A1 is parked next to a shell-pocked religious structure in or near Remagen, Germany, in March 1945. The gun mount is traversed to the rear, and the folding frontal panels of the gun shield are lowered. Jammed under the rear of the half-track is a motorcycle, which the vehicle appears to have driven over before parking.

(Air Defense Artillery Museum) Below: The crew of a Multiple Gun Motor Carriage M16 defending an approach to the Luden-dorff Bridge at Remagen goes about their duties as a truck full of German prisoners of war passes by. A German Jerrycan liq-uid container and bedrolls are lying on the ground adjacent to the M16. (NARA)

Above: "Rigor Mortis" is painted on the side of the shield of a Half-Track Combination Gun Motor Carriage M15A1 standing guard over a pontoon bridge over the Rhine River during the Ninth Army's advance in Germany on 25 March 1945. The vehicle is emplaced in an excavation up to the level of the top of its tracks. (Patton Museum) **Below:** A snapshot of a quad-50 machine-gun turret mounted in a Half-Track Multiple Gun Motor Carriage M16 shows a rear plate of the fighting compartment that lacks the usual stowage boxes. An identification star with a circle around it is partially hidden under the folding side plate. (12th Armored Division Memorial Museum)

Above: *The crew of an M16 nicknamed "DOZY DOATS II" are identified as, left to right: Boyer, Swartz, Lt. Hotra, Barney, and Sock. Hitched to the rear of the half-track is a 1-ton Ben Hur-type trailer with a tarpaulin over it. (12th Armored Division Memorial Museum)*

Below: *The M16 nicknamed "DOZY DOATS II" met an unfortunate end, apparently the victim of a mine or a shell. The rearward-pointing .50-caliber machine guns on the left side of the turret are visible at the bottom right of the photo. (12th Armored Division Memorial Museum)*

Above: *Members of a half-track-mounted 81mm mortar section pause during the shelling of enemy positions in a forest south of Colmar, France, on 3 February 1945. They were assigned to the 714th Tank Battalion, Combat Command B, 12th Armored Division. (NARA via Steve Zaloga)* **Below:** *Members of the 700th Military Police Company are manning this Half-*

Track Multiple Gun Motor Carriage M16 at a U.S. Army Border Guard base in Wanting, China, on 12 April 1945. The only visible markings on the vehicle are the recognition star on the left storage box on the rear and a small stencil on the body to the rear of the right door. "CO-A" is marked on one of the M2 ammunition chests. (NARA)

Above: *The quad .50-caliber machine guns of a Multiple Gun Motor Carriage M16 are being brought to bear on enemy forces near Ostiglia, Italy, on 24 April 1945. This vehicle and crew were assigned to the 432nd Antiaircraft Artillery Battalion, and they were firing across the Po River in support of U.S. Army Rangers. (NARA via Steve Zaloga)* **Below:** *The crew of an M15 Special multiple gun motor carriage with a 40mm Gun M1 of the 209th* Antiaircraft Artillery Battalion is prepared to engage Japanese forces along the Villa Verde Trail on Luzon in the Philippines on 8 May 1945. On these conversions, the gun shield was cut out to provide openings for the gun sights. This example has a section cut from the top of the shield attached over the left opening, spaced out slightly from the shield. Note the chains on the tires and the tracks for better traction. (Patton Museum)

Above: The same M15 Special of the 209th Antiaircraft Artillery Battalion that is seen in the preceding photo is viewed from a different angle during action on the Villa Verde Trail on 8 May 1945. This view and the preceding one provide good visual information on the large ammunition locker on the rear of the vehicle, including the padding on the inside of the lid and the two triangular braces under the locker. More details of the chains on the tracks also are apparent. (Patton Museum)

Below: The threat of enemy air attack was constant throughout the war in the Pacific. This Half-Track Car M2A1 is being employed for forward reconnaissance at a site overlooking Naha Airfield, Okinawa, on 12 June 1945. The vehicle is fitted with three whip antennas of different types. In addition to radio sets, the half-track carried telephone switchboard equipment, as evidenced by the communications wires routed to poles on the left side and the right rear corner of the vehicle. These likely led to dug in antiaircraft batteries, such as the ones in the following photographs. (NARA)

Above: *The crew of a well-entrenched Half-Track Combination Gun Motor Carriage M15A1 watches the sky for Japanese aircraft at Machinato, Okinawa, 12 June 1945. They were assigned to Battery D, M15 2nd Antiaircraft Artillery, 834th Aircraft Warning Battalion. The dome-shaped tops of the M2 ammunition chests for the .50-caliber guns have been removed. Note the simple, L-shaped hold-open latch on the bottom of the folding panel of the shield. (NARA)*

Below: *According to the original U.S. Army caption for this photograph, this battery of quad-.50-caliber machine guns on a Half-Track Multiple Gun Motor Carriage M16 entrenched along a shoreline on Okinawa was "constantly alerted" to fire on low-flying Japanese planes. The photo was taken around mid-June 1945. An additional, hand-operated Browning .50-caliber M2 HB machine gun is on a pedestal mount at the right front of the cab. (NARA)*

Above: *Members of Battery C, 834th Antiaircraft Artillery Battery, are manning a Half-Track Combination Gun Motor Carriage M15A1 at Yontan Airfield, Okinawa 7 June 1945. They were prepared for a possible Japanese attempt to retake the airfield. All of the men are identified: to the left front is Pvt. Russell Middendorf; to his rear are, left to right, Pfc. Forest E. Wilson, Pfc. Joe Marzano, Tech. 5 David Poli, Cpl. Robert W. Sporer, Pfc.*

Anthony A. Sapato, and Tech. 5 Donald M. Smith. (NARA)
Below: *A Half-Track Multiple Gun Motor Carriage M16 of the 209th Antiaircraft Artillery Automatic Weapons Battalion cooperates with Sherman tanks in providing fire support for elements of the 63rd Infantry Regiment during an attack on Japanese forces in Kiangen, northern Luzon, on 31 July 1945. (Patton Museum)*

Above: *Loaders make ready to replace ammunition chests on the quad .50-caliber machine guns of a Half-Track Multiple Gun Motor Carriage M16 of the 209th Antiaircraft Artillery Automatic Weapons Battalion. The vehicle was laying down fire against Japanese troops in the Cordon Sector of Luzon on 28 July 1945. To the right is an M7 Priest, which was lending support with its 105mm howitzer. (NARA)* **Below:** *An M16 Multiple Gun Motor Carriage, left, and a 40mm Gun Motor Carriage* M15 Special of the 209th Antiaircraft Artillery Battalion are deployed for fire support for elements of the 32nd Infantry Division near Yamashita Ridge on the Villa Verde Trail on Luzon, the Philippines, on 17 August 1945. Below the marking "A 232" on the rear stowage box of the M16, and repeated on the side of the fighting compartment of that vehicle, is what appears to be an insignia of a man, possibly a G.I., riding the chassis of a half-track in the manner of a child's scooter. (Steve Zaloga collection)

Chapter 7:
Field Use Post-WWII

New Roles for the WWII Machines

As noted in Part One of this series, even before victory was declared in Europe, half-track production had halted. Other, typically fully-tracked, vehicles filled many roles that had previously been the half-track's dominion. Many half-tracks were transferred to allies or disposed of as surplus. By 1947, most versions of the half-track had been declared obsolete. However, in some applications fully tracked replacements were developing slowly. In fact, at the outset of the Korean War the half-track still reigned supreme in the realm of Multiple Gun Motor Carriages.

While these had been conceived as antiaircraft weapons, which upon occasion during WWII had been used against ground targets, in Korea jet-powered aircraft outstripped the MGMC's capabilities. The new foe was found in the so-called human wave type of attacks pursued by the North Koreans. The withering firepower of half-tracks could stem these tides, but by then ammunition for the aging M15A1, as well as M16 half-tracks themselves, were in short supply.

To resolve the matter of the 37mm ammunition for the M1A2 main gun on the M15A1, the Army opted to discard the 37mm gun entirely, along with the coaxially mounted .50 caliber machine guns, in favor of the by-then ubiquitous 40mm Bofors. These conversions were done at the Tokyo Ordnance Depot, with the results initially designated T19, OCM 33894 of 15 September 1951 bestowed the designation M34 and classified the half-track as Limited Standard.

The Subcommittee on Automotive Equipment, on 10 February 1955, noted that 104 Carriages, Motor, Combination Gun, M15A1 had been converted to Gun, 40mm, Self-Propelled, M34. As of 10 February, Army stocks consisted of 72 M34 vehicles, all in the Far East Command. The same document noted that on the same date the Army held 498 M15A1 Combination Gun Motor Carriages worldwide, with 113 of these being stored unserviceable in the zone of interior, and that both the M15A1 and M34 be reclassified as Obsolete.

For service in Korea, the armor of the M45D mount of the M16 was augmented by folding gun shields attached to either side of the mount, providing some measure of protection for the loaders. This idea found favor with Ordnance, and ultimately standard designs of these so-called "bat-wings" were developed by Rock Island Arsenal.

To supplement the existing meager stocks of M16 Multiple Gun Motor Carriages, Bowen and McLaughlin, Inc., was contracted to modify 1,662 M3 Personnel Carriers to a configuration comparable to that of the M16.

Because the M3 lacked the folding armor of the M16, a different mount was used, the M45F. The M45F featured a 12-inch extension ring on the bottom, giving the mount the height to fire over the sides of the personnel carrier. A slip ring allowed interphone connection to be made for the gunner to the vehicle cab, as well as a field telephone on the rear of the vehicle. "Bat wing" armor was installed

Reserve Officers' Training Corps (ROTC) students from The Citadel in Charleston, South Carolina, are receiving training on the operation of the Half-Track Combination Gun Motor Carriage M15A1 at Fort Sheridan, Illinois, on 15 July 1947. The barrels of all three 37mm guns visible here are in an unpainted, polished-metal finish. (NARA)

on the mount. These vehicles, which retained the rear door of the M3, were classified as Substitute Standard on 24 April 1952 by OCM 34189 and designated M16A1.

Some of the features of the M16A1 were retro-fitted to 492 M16s, which were then redesignated M16A2 by OCM 34825 on 11 May 1953, and also classified as Substitute Standard. The M16A2

featured the rear door, as found on the M3, the bat wings and slip ring for interphone communications. The arrangement of stowage boxes on the rear of the vehicle was changed to accommodate the rear door.

The M16 was to be the longest-serving variant of half-track in the U.S. Army, not being declared obsolete until February 1958.

Above: *Two crewmen of a Half-Track Combination GMC M15A1 pose for their photograph during a training exercise at Fort Bliss, Texas, around 1949. The vehicle has markings on the bumper for the 50th Anti-aircraft Artillery Battalion. A whip antenna is mounted to the rear of the right door and is secured in a forward-pointing, horizontal position. (Air Defense Artillery Museum)*

Below: *On a firing range at Fort Bliss, Texas, around 1949, two crewmen of a Half-Track Combination GMC M15A1 are holding open the cover assemblies of the .50-caliber machine guns with one hand and gripping the charging handles with the other. Note the ring sights and the operating hand cranks at the bottom of the photo. (Air Defense Artillery Museum)*

Above: *The same gun mount in the Combination GMC M15A1 seen in the preceding photo is shown closer up, without the crewmen present. The view is from the lead-setter's position, between the two gun pointers' seats (traverse pointer left, elevation pointer right). The other crewmen were the squad leader, the driver, and two cannoneers that loaded the guns and made sure they were functioning properly. (Air Defense Artillery Museum)*

Left: *An M15A1 crewman poses on his vehicle during a training exercise at Fort Bliss, Texas, around 1949. The cylinder below the 37mm gun barrel is the recuperator assembly. The object that looks like a handle on the top front of this assembly is an expansion tube. (Air Defense Artillery Museum)*

Above: *A column of five Half-Track Multiple Gun Motor Carriages M16 prepare to depart from an exercise area in the Free Territory of Trieste, located between Italy and Yugoslavia, on 21 April 1950. The first vehicle is registration number 4050911. This group was part of the U.S. occupation force of the territory in the postwar years.* **Below:** *Two members of the crew of Half-Track Multiple GMC M16 registration number 4049396 stand to the rear of the quad .50-caliber machine gun mount during occupation duty in the Free Territory of Trieste on 21 April 1950. They were members of the 7178th General Depot Port Platoon. Marked on the left bumperette is "TRUST-7178-GDP," "TRUST" standing for Trieste United States Troops. (NARA, both)*

Above: *Half-tracks, including several M16 multiple gun motor carriages in the foreground with covers over their gun mounts, are on flatcars at Albuquerque, New Mexico, on 25 June 1950. The vehicles, assigned to the 21st Antiaircraft Artillery Automatic Weapons Battalion (SP), had just participated in Operation Sandex with the 80th Antiaircraft Artillery Group near Albuquerque and were about to depart for their home base at Fort Bliss, Texas.* **Below:** *Several half-tracks are in the foreground in this photo of the third-echelon maintenance area of the Ordnance Light Maintenance Company, 24th Infantry Division, near Kumchon, Korea, on 21 July 1950. To the left is registration number 4054982 1941-model Half-Track Personnel Carrier M3 retrofitted with a Maxson turret; the machine guns are dismounted and the turret is covered. At the center and right are two 40mm Gun Motor Carriages T19 (later designated M34), registration numbers 4050621 (a conversion of a Half-Track Multiple GMC M16) and 40100283. (NARA, both)*

Above: *Members of a Half-Track Combination Gun Motor Carriage M15A1 crew make adjustments to the vehicle somewhere in the Republic of Korea on 31 July 1950. The soldier to the right is working on the left headlight assembly, while the one to the far right is rigging an antenna cable. Lashed to the anti-ditching roller at the front of the vehicle is a water chest, used for circulating cooling water into the 37mm gun whenever necessary to prevent it from overheating. (NARA)*

Right: *Among the mass of vehicles and equipment loaded on closely packed landing craft in July 1950 is a Half-Track Combination Gun Motor Carriage M15A1 in the foreground along with wo others to the left of it and at the upper center of the photo. The nickname "Alcoa" is painted on the side of the camouflage-painted shield of the closer M15A1. A canvas curtain is strapped to the rear of the shield. Note the stacked five-gallon liquid containers to the left and the stowage bin on top of the raised armored windshield. (NARA)*

The crew of a Half-Track Combination Gun Motor Carriage M15A1 of the 25th Division warily scans the sky for signs of enemy aircraft in Korea in July 1950. The hinged frontal panels on each side of the armored shield are in the lowered positions. (Patton Museum)

Above: *This Half-Track Multiple Gun Motor Carriage M16 took a direct hit from a shell at the center of the side of the fighting compartment in Korea in August 1950. The registration number on the hood, 4079454, does not coincide with that of any vehicles built as M16s. Instead, this registration number pertained to a Half-Track Car M2 built under contract W-303-ORD-2080, although the body of the car is obviously the style that pertained to the Half-Track Personnel Carrier M3. (NARA)*

Right: *Two crewmen of a Half-Track Multiple Gun Motor Carriage M16 of the 92nd Antiaircraft Artillery Battalion in Korea on 2 September 1950 represent two key elements in successful antiaircraft defense: direct observation, in the form of the G.I. with the binoculars to the right, and radio communications for early warning, as symbolized by the man with the microphone and headphones to the left. Crews with visual and radio head's up were better able to react quickly to fast, low-flying enemy aircraft. (NARA)*

Above: *One crewman searches through binoculars while the rest of the crew of an M16 nicknamed "Old Expendable" take a break while defending a bridge near Tabu-dong, Republic of Korea, on 6 September 1950. They were members of the 92nd Antiaircraft Artillery Battery, attached to the 1st Cavalry Regiment. The vehicle's registration number, 4048404, pertained to a Multiple Gun Motor Carriage M13 with a twin .50-caliber* Maxson turret that was converted to a quad-.50-caliber machine gun turret. (Patton Museum) **Below:** *The crewmen of a half-track 81mm mortar carrier have set up their piece on the ground to the rear of their well-camouflaged vehicle, which is one of the models based on the Half-Track Car M2. A canvas shelter is rigged to the side of the vehicle, and there appears to be a tarpaulin over the fighting compartment. (NARA)*

Above: *A G.I. stands ready to observe through his binoculars as the gunner sits atop the turret of a Half-Track Multiple Gun Motor Carriage M16 around 1950. On the side of the fighting compartment is an insignia featuring a cartoon creature standing on a half-track bogie and track, holding a machine gun in each hand and with its tail wrapped around two more machine guns. (NARA)*

Right: *Ammunition loaders on the Half-Track Multiple Gun Motor Carriage M16 were very vulnerable to enemy fire, so during the Korean War, the 702nd Ordnance Company, 2nd Infantry Division, designed and constructed armored shields for the Maxson turrets. It was called "bat-wing" armor because of the hinged, folding side panels. An example from the 82nd Antiaircraft Artillery Battalion, 2nd Infantry Division, is seen in Korea on 24 March 1951. (NARA)*

The crew of a Half-Track 40mm Gun Motor Carriage M34 conducts a firing exercise along a shoreline. Note the semigloss sheen of the paint on the fender and the front wheel. A speed-ring sight is visible to the right of the 40mm gun barrel. (NARA)

Above: *An Army combat cameraman films an M16 crew providing covering fire for advancing troops on the west-central front in Korea on 30 March 1951. This vehicle, registration number 4050838, was manufactured under the first contract for M16s, W-303-ORD-1860. The vehicle and crew were assigned to Battery C, 21st Antiaircraft Artillery Battalion, 25th Infantry*

Division. **Below:** *Preparatory to reloading the machine guns of the same M16 depicted in the preceding photo, a crewman is ready to hand up a box of .50-caliber ammunition to the loaders on the vehicle. A large, nonstandard tub is strapped to the rear of the vehicle in the position where normally a bucket would be stored. (NARA, both)*

Above: A soldier is reloading the .50-caliber machine guns of another Multiple GMC M16 of Battery C, 21st Antiaircraft Artillery Battalion, on 30 March 1951 at the same location shown in the preceding photo. Belted ammunition is draped over the rear of the fighting compartment, and the tops of the ammunition chests are open for reloading. Ammo boxes are on the ground to the right of the vehicle. **Below:** In a photograph related to the preceding two images, two Half-Track Multiple GMCs M16 of Battery C, 21st Antiaircraft Artillery Battalion, fire at enemy forces during an advance of U.S. troops on the west-central front in Korea on 30 March 1951. The closer M16 is U.S. Army registration number 4049575 and is equipped with a bat-wing shield on the gun mount. Advancing across the field in the background are two Sherman medium tanks. (NARA, both)

Right: *The Turks were part of the United Nations forces that fought in the Korean War, and they fielded some U.S. military vehicles, such as this Half-Track Combination Gun Motor Carriage M15A1. This well-dug-in vehicle, flying a Turkish flag and bearing the nickname "BOZKURT," is standing guard in a valley in Korea on 14 March 1951. (NARA)*

Below: *A Multiple Gun Motor Carriage equipped with bat-wing armor on the quad gun turret returns enemy fire on the outskirts of Yanggu, Republic of Korea, on 15 April 1951. The vehicle and crew were assigned to the 15th Antiaircraft Artillery Battalion, 7th U.S. Division. An ammo trailer is hitched to the rear of the half-track. (NARA)*

Above: *Infantrymen slog down a road in Korea next to an M16 of the 21st Antiaircraft Artillery Battalion, 24th U.S. Infantry Division during an advance north of the Yong Pong Chon River on 23 April 1951. Ammunition boxes with .50-caliber ammo belts draped over them are stowed on the raised armored windshield. A rations box and more ammo boxes are on the front of the vehicle. (NARA)*

Left: *The winch on the front of a Half-Track Multiple Gun Motor Carriage M16 of Battery B, 15th Antiaircraft Artillery Battalion, 7th Infantry Division, is being used to recover an overturned 105mm howitzer in a mountain pass in Korea on 23 May 1951. On the side of the half-track is the nickname "Rotation Blues." The side panel of the bat-wing shield is in the folded-back position. (NARA)*

Above: *A Half-Track Multiple GMC M16 is firing on North Korean forces in support of an advance of the 17th Regimental Combat Team, 7th Infantry Division, on 20 May 1951. The nickname "Carol Lee" is painted on the bumper and on the driver's door. A box and a roll of barbed wire in the shape of a figure-8 are stowed on the front of the vehicle. This half-track was* registration number 4050150, produced under contract W-303-ORD-1860. **Below:** *Members of a Multiple Gun Motor Carriage M16 crew watch for signs of Chinese patrols near Uijong-Bu in Korea on 26 May 1951. Members of the 92nd Antiaircraft Artillery Battalion, 1st Cavalry Division, they were, left to right, Pfc. James T. Lewton, Pfc. Arthur Brogens, and Pfc. Lewis Desenti. (NARA, both)*

Above: *Members of Battery B, 256th Antiaircraft Artillery Battalion, pose with their M16 at Camp Rucker, Alabama, on 12 June 1951. They are, left to right, a Pvt. Alan; Cpl. Harry Maw; Pvt. Willis Hollingsworth; Pvt. Don Salemi; Pvt. Roger Robron; and Pvt. Erwin Wagner. Although not visible in this photo, hitched to this half-track was a towed 40mm Bofors gun.*
Below: *The quad .50-caliber machine guns of an M16 with* bat-wing armor on the gun mount are firing at a target during Operation Pipedream, a mock battle in Korea on 18 June 1951. The vehicle and crew were part of the 26th Antiaircraft Artillery Battalion, 5th Regimental Combat Team, 24th Infantry Division. This M16 was registration number 4050447. Belted .50-caliber ammunition is draped over the right shoulder of the loader to the left. (NARA, both)

Right: *Sergeant 1st Class Timothy P. Mounk of Greenville, Texas, pauses from reading a letter from home while the Texas state flag flies from his Half-Track Multiple Gun Motor Carriage M16 in Korea on 1 July 1951. Sergeant Mounk was serving with the 24th Infantry Division. (NARA)*

Below: *Private 1st Class Richard L. Jenkins of Richmond, Virginia, takes a turn at guard duty on a Multiple Gun Motor Carriage M15 near Hudong-Ni, Korea, on 14 July 1951. Personal packs are strapped to the folded-down panel of the fighting compartment. The top and the middle sign on the stake read, "STOP / FRONT / LINES" and "HAVE NO FEAR / THE 21ST AAA / IS HERE," a reference to the 21st Antiaircraft Artillery Battalion. (NARA)*

A Half-Track 40mm Gun Motor Carriage M34, registration number 40150170, of Battery B, 140th Antiaircraft Artillery Battalion, 40th U.S. InfantryDivision, drives by during a review at Camp Schimmelpfennig, Japan, on 30 September 1951. The new designation M34 had been bestowed on this vehicle two weeks before, on 15 September; formerly it was designated the Half-Track 40mm Gun Motor Carriage T19. (NARA)

The crew of a Half-Track Multiple GMC M16 of the 256th Antiaircraft Artillery Battalion, 47th U.S. Infantry Division, search the sky for signs of aggressor aircraft during Exercise Long Horn, a joint Army-Air Force maneuver at Fort Hood, Texas, on 2 April 1952. In addition to a radio set and antenna mounted in the vehicle, there is a portable radio and antenna to the left rear of the cab. (NARA)

Left: The nickname "Quad Lightning," surrounded by thunderbolts, is emblazoned on the side of this Half-Track Multiple Gun Motor Carriage M16 emplaced in a hull-down position. Two recognition stars are painted on the boxes on the rear of the vehicle. Behind an embankment to the right is an M4A3E8 medium tank. (NARA)

Below: Using a new Army method of loading a half-track on a railroad car, a Half-Track Combination Gun Motor Carriage M15A1 and a hitched trailer are secured to a flatcar at Kaftertal, West Germany, on 24 November 1953. The half-track has markings for the 62nd Antiaircraft Artillery Battalion, Seventh U.S. Army. (NARA)

Above: *Members of Battery D, 47th Division Artillery, are gathered around an entrenched Half-Track Multiple Gun Motor Carriage M16A1 at an undisclosed location on 11 December 1953. The unit markings on the bumper are spattered with mud and are illegible.* **Below:** *Members of the crew of a Half-Track Multiple Gun Motor Carriage M16 with bat-wing armor on the Maxson turret pose with several South Korean counterparts at an unidentified site in the Republic of Korea on 11 December 1953. Camouflage netting has cast a pattern on the side and rear of the half-track. (NARA, both)*

Above: *An M16 multiple GMC is engaging enemy forces in Korea in 1953. On the side of the fighting compartment just to the rear of the cab is stenciled "HELL'S FIRE." A small insignia that appears to be that of the 24th Infantry Division is below it. Gunners often folded down the two middle plates of the batwing armor for a better field of vision.* **Below:** *The guns of an M16 fire on enemy forces near White Horse Ridge in Korea in* 1953. Ammo boxes are piled on top of the cab and the hood as well as on the ground to the right. On the side of the fighting compartment is a fading nickname, "QUAD LIGHTNING," with small representations of thunderbolts on each side. These markings are identical to those seen a few pages back in a 1951 photo of an M16, but it is uncertain if this was a stencil applied to several vehicles or markings particular to a single M16. (NARA, both)

Above: *At a base in the Republic of Korea, Eugene C. Redding, left, of Battery C, 26th Antiaircraft Artillery Battalion, 24th U.S. Infantry Division, instructs members of the Filipino 2nd Battalion Combat Team, attached to the 24th U.S. Infantry Division, in assembling Browning M2 HB .50-caliber machine guns on 4 May 1954. In the background are two Multiple Gun Motor Carriages M16: registration numbers 404977, left, and 40172414. (NARA)*

Below: *A Multiple GMC M16, registration number 4049506, assigned to the 29th Antiaircraft Artillery Battalion, Automatic Weapons Group, is on display at an Organization Day celebration at Camp Chitose No. 1, Hokkaido, Japan, on 8 June 1954. On Organization Day, once a year an Army unit would stand down and enjoy a day of games, food, entertainment, and relaxation. The sign on the front bumper reads "EXPLOSIVES" in English and Japanese. (NARA)*

Above: *A column of armed M16 Multiple Gun Motor Carriages rolls through the streets of Hachinohe, Irate Prefecture, Japan on 30 August 1954. The vehicles are part of the 29th AAA Battalion, 1st Cavalry Division, and the unit is relocating to Camp Haugen, nearby, following the transfer of the 29th's former base at Hokkaido to the newly-formed Japanese Self Defense Forces.* **Below:** *A Combination Gun Motor Carriage M15A1 with complete gun mount installed (foreground) and a half-track—apparently an M16—with the guns dismounted from a quad-.50-caliber machine-gun turret are parked at the Camp Kasumigaura Ordnance Depot, Ibaragi Prefecture, Japan, on 18 January 1955. The U.S. Army recently had transferred these two vehicles to the Japanese Ground Defense Forces. The U.S. Army markings on them have been painted over and Japanese markings have been applied. (NARA, both)*

Above: *A Corporal Joseph Krob assembles the radio antenna on this M16 as the rest of the crew prepares to fire the quad fifty during a training exercise at Kadena Air Base, Okinawa on 11 February 1955. Clearly visible atop the receiver of lower .50 caliber machine gun is the firing solenoid and electrical lead. All four guns were similarly equipped on the M16 as the weapons were electrically fired.* **Below:** *A crew of Battery A, 29th*

Antiaircraft Artillery Battalion, 1st U.S. Cavalry Division, make ready to fire the .50-caliber machine guns of an M16 during a demonstration at the firing range near Missawa Air Base, Japan, on 23 April 1955. The vehicle is registration number 4049194. Note the sandbags piled on the track suspension and the open lids of the ammunition chests, with the ends of the ammo belts hanging out of them. (NARA, both)

Above: *The crew of a Multiple Gun Motor Carriage M16 of the 453rd Antiaircraft Artillery Battalion (Automatic Weapons) conducts a training exercise at Locust Point Antiaircraft Artillery Range along the shore of Lake Erie near Camp Perry, Ohio, on 22 June 1955. The stencil on the interior of the folded-down plate on the fighting compartment is a warning to lower the folding shield before releasing the zero-depression stop of the gun mount. (NARA)*

Left: *Officers of the 1st Cavalry Division and the 29th Antiaircraft Artillery Battalion inspect an M42 Duster, left, with a half-track with a quad .50-caliber machine gun turret—apparently a Multiple Gun Motor Carriage M16—in the background. The scene was at Camp Haugen, in northern Honshu, Japan, on 25 July 1955. (NARA)*

Left: *A Private Landtroop of Battery C, 65th Antiaircraft Artillery Battalion, performs routing maintenance on a Browning .50-caliber machine gun on a quad gun turret at a base in Okinawa on 22 August 1955. By this time, jet aviation had rendered gun mounts such as this as ineffective, but the Army still maintained an inventory of these mounts for defense against slower, low-flying threats. (NARA)*

Right: *The quad .50-caliber gun turret on this Multiple Gun Motor Carriage M16 had been raised from the floor of the fighting compartment to the top of the compartment. The vehicle and crew were assigned to Battery D, 29th Antiaircraft Artillery Battalion, and the photo was taken during practice firing at Misawa "A" Range in northern Honshu, Japan, on 16 August 1955. (NARA)*

Chapter 8:
Three-Quarter Tracks

The Stepchild of the Half-Track

The SNL G102 family of half-tracks as discussed in the bulk of this volume, as well as the previous volume, had scarcely entered production before efforts had begun to create a half-track vehicle with improved mobility and increased capacity.

In order to increase both load-carrying capacity and floatation, and tolerate an increase in weight, the resultant vehicle was essentially a three-quarter track, even though the Army retained the half-track nomenclature.

The initial effort in this area was made by Mack, who utilized the tracks and suspension of the M2 light tank in creating a vehicle, which bore 80% of its weight on the tracks, the remaining 20% being supported by the non-driving front axle. Mack estimated that the pilot vehicle could be produced in three months, and the cost would be $15,200.00. The Ordnance Committee, through action 16313, recommended that such a vehicle be procured, and provided the designation Chassis, Half Track, T3. The vehicle was ordered in December 1940 and completed in October 1941.

Powered by a Mack EY gasoline engine, the same model as used in the Mack NO, the vehicle was driven from Mack's Allentown, Pennsylvania plant to the Army's Aberdeen, Maryland proving ground. While in the NO the engine had a single carburetor and developed 176 horsepower, dual carburetors were included in the T3 installation, with the resultant increase of horsepower to 192. The engine was coupled to a five-speed transmission,

two auxiliary transmission and a controlled differential. Steering was through a combination of the conventional truck front axle and the controlled differential track steering.

The vehicle was fitted with power takeoff driven front-mounted, 28,000-pound capacity self-recovery winch. This winch was deemed by Aberdeen personnel "invaluable as an aid in operation through severe field conditions."

While the original intention was that this vehicle would be used as a prime mover, notably for the 105mm howitzer, The body included provisions for seating ten men. However, coincidentally the 40mm Bofors anti-aircraft gun was becoming available about the same time as the T3 was gaining momentum.

The idea was soon broached to mount the weapon on the large T3. Such an alternation was authorized by OCM 16801 on 5 June 1941. This provided for the mounting of the weapon, its Kerrison Director and associated power plant on the Mack chassis.

After the initial testing of the T3 was completed, which indicated that the vehicle had excellent performance, the vehicle was modified, becoming the 40mm Gun Motor Carriage T1.

Testing of the T1 at Aberdeen in December 1941 proved that mounting the gun and director on the same chassis was impractical, due to interference between the units and lack of stability. Consideration was also given to mounting the M2A1 105mm howitzer on this chassis, and drawings of such a vehicle were prepared in November 1941. The T1 was shipped back to Mack, who returned the vehicle to

Above: *Even before the United States entered World War II, the Army and the private sector were seeking to field half-tracks with better cross-country performance and greater carrying capacity. Mack Manufacturing Corporation developed a design for a vehicle with a rear engine, enabling a long-base track with minimal space between the front of the track and the front wheels. The Mack-produced design was designated the Half-Track T3 and is shown during tests at Aberdeen Proving Ground on 13 October 1941. (Patton Museum)*

Below: *The Half-Track T3 is seen from the left side at Aberdeen on 13 October 1941. Because of the presence of the front wheel wells to the sides of the cab, the entry door was to the rear of the driver's seat, and to the rear of the folding side panel of the cab. This entry door was of the same arrangement on the right side of the vehicle. (Chris Benedict collection)*

T3 configuration. Owing to further development of the G-102 series vehicles as well as fully tracked prime movers and motor carriages, the T3 program was cancelled on 4 June 1942 by OCM 18321, and along with it the T34 program, as the 105mm-armed Mack half-track had been dubbed.

Still another effort at increasing performance and floatation was the Autocar T16. Based on the M2, the T16 featured an extended frame, new suspension and longer, wider tracks, as well as an armored roof. Autocar completed the pilot in November 1941.

The ground contact length of the track was increased about 30% and the width 2 inches, thereby reducing ground pressure. However, the increased weight brought about by the longer suspension and frame, ¼-inch thick armored roof and the larger track, combined with the unchanged drive train of a M2, resulted in degraded performance. Accordingly work on the Autocar M2-based T16 was stopped and the lessons learned applied to a new large half-track program.

That program was a result of OCM 17203 of 11 September 1941, with the objective being to satisfy a request from the Field Artillery branch for a larger prime mover for the 105mm howitzer. The vehicle was to accommodate 14 men, and was expected to feature an automatic transmission. Designated the T14, the vehicle was projected to weigh 10 tons, including a 5,600-pound payload. Significantly, it was to be proof against .30-caliber ammunition from all sides and the top, and have a road speed of 45 miles per hour.

The following month the Half-Track Vehicle Committee reviewed the Ordnance Committee's T14 requirements and determined that they were unattainable within the weight desired. Accordingly, the T14 project was abandoned.

In its place the Committee proposed the concurrent development of five new designs, designated T15 through T19. The proposed characteristics of each were:

T15—proposed by White on 31 March 1942, powered by a front-mounted White 24AX 12-cylinder horizontally opposed 210 horsepower engine driving through a Spicer synchromesh transmission with power shift. The vehicle was to be equipped with a powered front axle, and cost was given at $34,000 without tracks.

T16—proposed by Diamond T on 26 February 1942, powered by a front-mounted Hercules RXLD gasoline or General Motors 6-71 Diesel engine, driving through a Spicer automatic transmission. The vehicle would feature a powered front axle, but the design was such that should this expense not be warranted, a non-powered axle could easily be incorporated instead. This vehicle had a midships—mounted underbody self-recovery winch, its cable able to be played out either forward or to the rear.

T17—Initially proposed by Autocar, to be powered by a front-mounted Hercules RXLD engine coupled to 4-speed Spicer synchromesh transmission and include a powered front axle.

T18—Rear mounted General Motors 6-71 Diesel engine, driving through a Spicer or GM 5-speed synchromesh transmission with power shift. Non-powered front axle. M3 light tank suspension.

T19—proposed by Mack, powered by a rear-mounted White 24AX engine driving through a Spicer or GM 5-speed synchromesh transmission with power shift. Non-powered front axle. M3 light tank suspension.

All of these vehicles were expected to accommodate 14 men, including the driver, adhere to a maximum weight of 16 tons, including a payload capacity of 3 tons. This would allow the vehicle to transport 40 rounds of 105mm or 3-inch antitank as well as 400 rounds of .50-caliber machine gun ammunition. The machine gun ammunition was for use through the mounted .50-caliber machine gun. Maximum speed was established to be at least 35 MPH on level road while fully loaded.

Even before development was begun, the T15 was dropped as it was felt to be too similar to the T17. Rather, in May 1942 the Office of the Chief of Ordnance directed that the two designs be combined, taking the best features of each. Two T17

Above: *As seen in another 13 October 1941 photo, the cab of the Half-Track T3 has a sloped frontal plate with a single-piece armored windshield. The brush guards were rather massive considering the size of the service headlights. A winch was mounted above the front bumper. The front wheels of the T3 were not driven but were linked to the differential steering of the tracks. (TACOM LCMC History Office)*

Below: *The U.S. Army report on the testing of the Half-Track T3 mentioned that the Gar Wood winch was "invaluable as an aid in operation through severe field conditions." The driver's rear-view mirror was mounted on the left side of the top frame of the windshield. Three hold-open supports for the ¼-inch-thick armored windshield are below the windshield. (NARA)*

pilots were commissioned, the White and Autocar firms agreeing each to build a single prototype at a cost of $35,000.00 each.

Both vehicles were to be powered by White 24AX horizontally opposed engines. Pilot number one would be built by White, with Autocar building pilot number two. The Autocar T17 was shipped to Aberdeen in time for a demonstration on 25 June 1943, while the White pilot was sent to the Armored Force Board at Fort Knox.

The intent was that a competitive test be held between examples of all three half-tracks at Fort Knox. However, a letter from Army Ground Forces on 29 January 1944 cancelled the tests before they could be completed.

As with the T15, the T18 was scrubbed before production. This decision was made owing to Army policy concerning Diesel engines.

Diamond T produced two pilots of the T16, while Mack produced two T19s, which not surprisingly had considerable resemblance to the earlier T3. According to OCM documents from April 1942, the two Diamond T T16s cost $21,344 each, not including their torque convertor transmissions, and those transmissions would cost more than the half-tracks.

Rather than the White 24AX engine, Mack used the Continental R6572 6-cylinder engine—but it remained the only one of the new group to lack a powered front axle. Mack completed the first pilot in December 1942. It was first subjected to engineering tests at the General Motors Proving Ground, then was sent back to Mack for reconditioning prior to delivery to Aberdeen Proving Ground.

The first T16 pilot was completed in March 1943, and after undergoing 1200 miles of testing by Autocar, was shipped to Fort Bragg on 28 May 1943. Initial testing indicated that the vehicle provided satisfactory operation, it lacked sufficient engine horsepower. However, before the Board could complete testing of the T16, the decision had been made to concentrate on high-speed tractors, forgoing half-tracks and trucks as prime movers.

Testing of each type of the three pilots was also conducted at Aberdeen Proving Ground, including a 5,000-mile endurance test. This test began 1 July 1943, and owing to several major component failures as well as a low priority due to Artillery's decision in June 1943 to pursue high-speed tractors, Aberdeen's endurance test was not completed until 27 June 1944.

By that time Field Artillery's preference for fully tracked vehicles was clear, and OCM items 26107 and 26351 of 21 December 1944 and 11 January 1945 respectively closed the development project on the T16, T17 and T19. As it turned out, this also closed development of U.S. Army half-tracks.

Above: *On the rear of the Half-Track T3 was a large ventilation grille with 11 armored shutters. An Army test report indicated that when the shutters were closed for maximum protection, "partial engine cooling will still be obtained." Mounted in the rear of the vehicle was a Mack EY six-cylinder, 707-c.i. engine with dual carburetors. The engine was rated at 192 horsepower. (NARA)*

Below: *The shutters are closed on the Half-Track T3 in this photo taken at Aberdeen Proving Ground on 13 October 1941. To close the shutters, it was necessary to do so from outside of the vehicle. The Army test report on the T3 recommended that a means of controlling the shutters from inside the vehicle be devised. (NARA)*

Above: *The Mack EY six-cylinder, 707-c.i. engine in the Half-Track T3 is viewed from the left side with the bodywork of the vehicle removed. In the foreground is the left track. Below the finned exhaust manifold are the dual carburetors. Below the rear carburetor is the distributor. Below the front carburetor is* the air compressor. **Below:** *On the right side of the Mack EY engine, as installed on a Half-Track T3 chassis, are, left to right, the generator, two FRAM oil filters, and the Delco-Remy starter. To the far left is the radiator. (NARA, both)*

Above: A Mack Manufacturing Corporation photograph depicts the radiator-fan mount and radiator shroud on a Half-Track T3 chassis. The black side and top of the radiator is visible to the front of the shroud. An A-frame supported the fan, and a series of pulleys, belts, and shafts drove the fan. **Below:** The Half-Track T3 chassis is viewed from the front left. This vehicle had steel bogie wheels with no rubber tires. According to the U.S. Army's report of the testing of the T3, the steel wheels increased the vehicle's rolling resistance and was largely responsible for the blowing-out of track blocks. The report recommended substituting wheels with rubber tires. (NARA, both)

Above: This Mack Manufacturing Corporation photograph provides an excellent idea of the layout of the Half-Track T3 chassis. In the foreground are the rear bumper, the radiator and fan, and the engine. To the front of the engine are the transmission and the final-drive assembly for the tracks. To the front are the steering wheel, gear-shift levers, and Gar Wood winch. (NARA)

Left: The Half-Track T3 chassis is seen from the front right. Two of the several deficiencies the Army tests of the T3 disclosed were that there was excessive kickback in the steering wheel when operating over undulating terrain, and the vehicle was rear-heavy because of the location of the engine, placing excessive weight on the two rear bogie assemblies. (NARA)

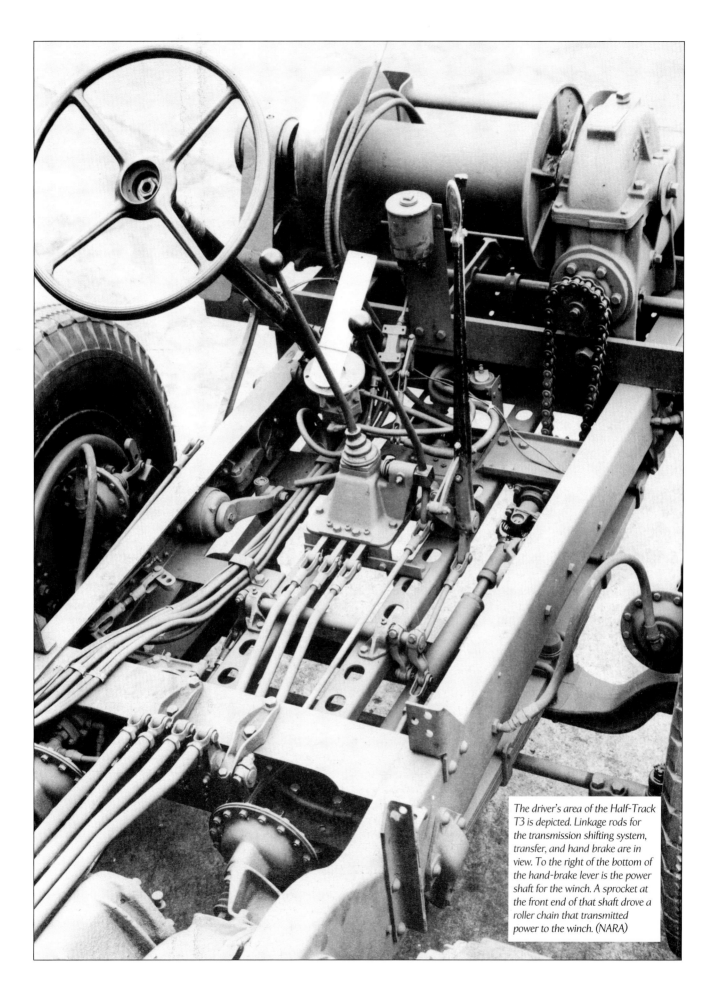

The driver's area of the Half-Track T3 is depicted. Linkage rods for the transmission shifting system, transfer, and hand brake are in view. To the right of the bottom of the hand-brake lever is the power shaft for the winch. A sprocket at the front end of that shaft drove a roller chain that transmitted power to the winch. (NARA)

Above: *After Ordnance Department tests indicated the T3 was generally satisfactory for operational service, the chassis was reworked to enable installation of a 40mm Automatic Gun M1 and its related Director M5, also called the Kerriston Director. The resulting vehicle was designated the Half-Track 40mm Gun Motor Carriage T1, and the basic pilot for that half-track, less the 40mm gun and director, is seen on 5 December 1941 at Aberdeen Proving Ground. This vehicle was assigned* registration number W-609057. **Below:** *In a right-side view of the basic pilot for the Half-Track 40mm Gun Motor Carriage T1, the fuel tank and the compartment housing the 192 horse-power engine are at the rear of the vehicle. Crew seats were installed, including two inward-facing ones to the front of the engine compartment. It is clear that the suspension and tracks of this vehicle were much more robust than those of the basic M2 and M3 half-track families. (Patton Museum, both)*

Above: *Above the right front wheel of the basic pilot of the Half-Track 40mm Gun Motor Carriage T1, as seen in a 5 December 1941 photo at Aberdeen, was a platform for the Director M5. To the rear of the driver's seat is the platform for the 40mm Gun M1. All of the seat backs except for the driver's have been folded down.* **Below:** *A G.I. stands next to the rear of* the basic pilot of the Half-Track 40mm Gun Motor Carriage T1 on 5 December 1941 at Aberdeen. A large grille dominated the rear of the engine compartment. To each side of the grille was a small, hinged door, a taillight assembly, and a piece of sheet metal that apparently served as a mudguard. Below the grille on the bumper was a tow pintle. (Patton Museum, both)

Above: The left side of the engine compartment of the basic pilot of the Half-Track 40mm Gun Motor Carriage T1 had two columns of horizontal louvers. The fuel tank on the right side of the engine compartment was not repeated on the left side. The idler wheels were six-spoke, while the bogie wheels were five-spoke. (Patton Museum)

Left: The basic pilot for the 40mm GMC T1 lacked a front winch. Two braces made of channel steel extended from the front of the body to the front bumper. Inboard of the steering wheel are the platform for the director and the rear of a crew seat. The front axle and leaf springs are visible. (Patton Museum)

Right: As seen in a 5 December 1941 photograph at Aberdeen Proving Ground, the rear bumper of the basic pilot for the 40mm GMC T1 had a forward-pointing bow in the center where the tow pintle was located. The two small doors to the sides of the grille each had two leaf hinges on the inboard side. (Patton Museum)

Below: By 8 December 1941, as photographed at Aberdeen Proving Ground, the basic pilot Half-Track 40mm Gun Motor Carriage T1, registration number W-609057, had been fitted with a 40mm Automatic Gun M1 and a Director M5. The director is on the front right of the vehicle, and the gun mount is to the rear between the director and the engine compartment. (Patton Museum)

Above: *Although the idea of having a 40mm gun and its director on a common vehicle was sound, it is obvious in this view of the right side of the Half-Track 40mm Gun Motor Carriage T1 that the director was in the way of the gun, as were the structures to the rear of the gun.* **Below:** *A soldier stands next to the rear of the Half-Track 40mm Gun Motor Carriage T1 at* Aberdeen Proving Ground on 8 December 1941. A generator unit had been added to the vehicle to the left front of the engine compartment, to supply power to the director and the mechanisms on the gun mount that enabled the director to remotely control the gun. (Patton Museum, both)

Above: *The locations of the director, the generator, and the engine compartment severely limited the ability of the 40mm gun to engage fast, low-flying aerial targets. In addition, tests at Aberdeen Proving Ground disclosed that the vibration of the gun during firing diminished the accuracy of the Director M5. The proximity of the gun to the director also sometimes interfered with the director's field of vision. (Patton Museum)*

Below: *The generator assembly on the Half-Track 40mm GMC T1 is seen from a different angle. To the front of the right seat of the gun mount are the manual elevation hand cranks and, farther forward, the oil gear for effecting the powered elevation of the gun. Similar arrangements on the left side of the mount effected the manual and power traverse of the piece. (TACOM LCMC History Office)*

Left: *Although the 40mm gun on the 40mm GMC T1 could be operated manually by crewmen seated on the gun mount, the more accurate method of firing the gun at aircraft was through the director on the front of the vehicle. An operator sat on each side of the director, using telescopes and hand wheels to track the target in azimuth and elevation, and a range setter fed estimated range data into the director. The director then calculated a firing solution and transmitted it to the gun mount to remotely control the gun. (Patton Museum)*

Below: *In a rear view of the 40mm Gun Motor Carriage T1, visible above the rear of the engine compartment are, left to right, the generator unit, the gun sights and their supports and the cover for the automatic feed of the 40mm Automatic Gun M1, and the top of the Director M5. (Patton Museum)*

Above: *An elevated view of the 40mm GMC T1 parked among a mass of other vehicles at Aberdeen Proving Ground on 8 December 1941 offers a better view of the tops of the structures to the rear of the gun mount. An instrument panel and controls are on a dashboard to the front of the steering wheel. Following testing of the vehicle at Aberdeen, during which serious deficiencies were detected, the T1 program was discontinued. (Patton*

Museum) **Below:** *The Autocar-produced Half-Track Car T16, as seen at Aberdeen Proving Ground on 3 February 1942,s was an attempt to develop an improved Half-Track Car M2. It featured a longer chassis frame, lengthened and widened tracks, redesigned bogie assemblies, and an armored top. An opening at the front of the armored top allowed for firing a .50-caliber machine gun to the front. (NARA)*

Above: Compared to the Half-Track Car M2, the Half-Track Car T16 featured larger bogie wheels and a redesigned bogie assembly with longer arms and two sets of track-support rollers on top. The idler wheels were mounted on the extended chassis frame. The vertical supports of the armored top were gusseted at the bottom. **Below:** For the rear of the body of the Half-Track Car T16, the lower part of the body of the Half-Track Car M2 was detached and moved farther to the rear, with steel plates on top and to the sides to secure that section to the upper part of the rear of the body. A tripod for the .50-caliber machine gun (top) and the two .30-caliber machine guns were stowed on the rear. The frontal plate of the armored top had a hinged section in the center that could be folded back, and there were hinged plates on the sides and the rear of the top; all of these plates are shown folded back and stacked. (NARA, both)

Above: *In a photo of the Half-Track Car T16 from the same angle, the front and rear folding plates of the armored top are in their normal positions. The rear plate was supported by a diagonal brace on each side. At the tops of the support columns for the armored top were gussets, on the front and the rear of each column, oriented at right angles to the gussets on the bottoms of the columns. (NARA)*

Right: *In a rear view of the Half-Track Car T16 taken at Aberdeen Proving Ground on 3 January 1942, a better idea is available of the width of the hinged side panels on the armored top, shown folded up here. (NARA)*

Above: The Half-Track Car T16 was assigned U.S. Army registration number W-4017058. The armored top presumably would have offered some protection to the crew from shrapnel and splinters from airburst shells, but the open sides would have left the crew vulnerable to fire and shell bursts to the sides. **Below:** In an elevated view of the Half-Track Car T16, all of the hinged panels of the armored top are folded back.

Folding these plates back offered the crew in the fighting compartment better visibility at the expense of diminished protection. On top of the stack of folded plates is the front plate, actually two plates with a joint in the middle. The opening in the center of the frontal plates had an extension on the left side to accommodate the .50-caliber machine gun's ammunition box. (NARA, both)

Above: *The hinged plates on the Half-Track Car T16 are all in their normal positions. The side plates each had three hinges. The two frontal plates each had two hinges, and the rear plate had four hinges. In addition to the two braces on the underside of the rear panel, this panel had on top what appear to have been two sliding-type stops, to help support the panel. (NARA)*

Right: *As seen from the rear in a 3 January 1942 Aberdeen Proving Ground photo, one can imagine that, with the open rear and the closed front of the fighting compartment of the Half-Track Car T16, the interior of the vehicle would have become a very dangerous place when under fire from the rear, with bullets or shrapnel ricocheting off the frontal armor. (NARA)*

In an elevated rear view of the Half-Track Car T16 with all of the hinged armored plates folded back, a better view is available of the shape of the opening for the .50-caliber machine gun in the frontal plates. Visible inside the fighting compartment are the two ammunition storage compartments. (NARA)

The Half-Track Car T16 is viewed from the front with all hinged panels folded back. The structure at the front of the armored top of the T16 included a fixed, armored wing on each side. These were pentagonal in shape, tapering at the bottom. (NARA)

Left: *Both of the hinged frontal panels of the armored top of the Half-Track Car T16 are lowered. Information is not available on the range of movement of the .50-caliber machine gun when the armored panels were lowered, but one may surmise that it was quite limited. (NARA)*

Below: *Half-Track Cars T16, left, and M2 are parked back to back to illustrate the design differences between them. The Half-Track Car T16 was discontinued because of deficiencies in the armor roof and the suspension, but test results from this program were applied to the development of the Half-Track Trucks T15 through T19. (NARA)*

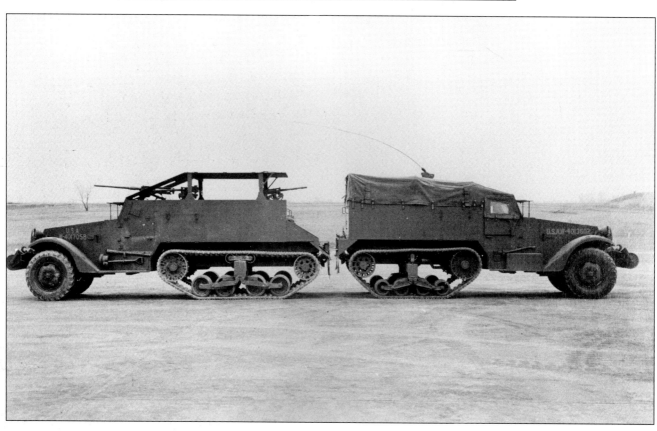

Above: The Half-Track Truck T16 was one of five half-track trucks proposed for development at a meeting of the Half-Track Vehicle Committee on 20 October 1941. These were to be designated Half-Track Trucks T15, T16, T17, T18, and T19. The T15 and T18 were discontinued before development of them began. All were to be artillery prime movers for guns and howitzers up to 6,500 pounds and with a carrying capacity of approximately 5,600 pounds including 14 personnel. They were to have armor proof against 30-caliber bullets and were to be armed with a .50-caliber machine gun. Shown here at Aberdeen Proving Ground on 25 June 1943 one of two pilot Half-Track Trucks T16 built by Diamond T Motor Car Company, registration number 4015651. **Below:** A six-foot measuring stick is propped up against the right rear corner of the Half-Track Truck T16 at Aberdeen during tests on 25 June 1943. To accommodate the extended tracks, each bogie assembly included six pairs of bogie wheels. Two sets of track-support rollers were above each bogie frame. The rear of the body resembled that of the Half-Track Personnel Carrier M3 and M5 families, with a centrally located door above a tow pintle and two bumperettes. (Patton Museum, both)

Above: *The other pilot Half-Track Truck T16 produced by Diamond T, registration number 4015650, is seen from the right rear with a tarpaulin and cab top installed during analysis by the Armored Force Board Test Operation at Fort Knox, Kentucky. The band-type tracks were of similar construction to those used on half-track cars and personnel carriers, but longer and with a width of 14 inches.* **Below:** *Half-Track Truck T16 registration number 4015650 is seen from the left front during tests at Fort Knox. The vehicle had a bottom-hinged armored windshield, armored shutters in front of the radiator, removable headlight assemblies, an anti-ditching roller, and, to the right of the roller, an opening and guides for a winch cable. The vehicle was powered by a Hercules RXLD gasoline engine, but a General Motors 6-71 Diesel engine could be substituted. (Kevin Emdee collection, both)*

Above: *One of the two pilot Half-Track Trucks T16 displays no visible markings in this photograph. The detachable-type headlight assemblies are mounted. The anti-ditching roller seems to have been mounted on spindles attached to the split front bumper. The armored windshield constituted two panels, each with three hinges at the bottom. On each panel, the hinges except for the center one were equipped with coil springs to assist in raising and lowering the panel. (NARA)*

Below: *The same pilot Half-Track Truck T16 shown in the preceding photo is seen during tests on the suspension, the left track having been driven over a stack of wooden blocks. The absence of a U.S.A. number on the vehicle and the fact that the driver is in civilian clothing suggests that the photo was taken during manufacturer's tests at the Diamond T Motor Company plant. The C-shaped profile of the split front bumper of the Half-Track Truck T16 is visible from this angle. (NARA)*

Left: *The rear of the body of the Half-Track Truck T16 was reminiscent of an enlarged and wider Half-Track Personnel Carrier M3 body, with its central door, curved bumperettes with a tow pintle between them, grab handles to the sides, and mud flaps. (NARA)*

Below: *The rear door of a pilot Half-Track Truck T16 is open, showing the inside of the door and permitting a limited view into the fighting compartment. A pedestal for a machine gun is visible inside. To the right of the pedestal in the background is a seat back. (NARA)*

Above: *Some details of the interior of one of the pilot Half-Track Trucks T16 are available in this overhead shot. Fuel tanks are in the front of the cargo compartment, to the rear of which are bench seats and seat backs with stowage bins behind them, and ammunition storage compartments. The lid of the left ammo compartment is open, and one of the fiberboard packing tubes for an artillery round is leaning out. Behind that packing tube is a round retainer for the tube, in the flipped-up position. Also note the substantial framing of the windshield.* **Below:**

The second model half-track truck for which a pilot vehicle was produced was the T17, seen in a 25 June 1947 Aberdeen Proving Ground photo. Autocar and White each built a pilot vehicle, and the one shown here is the second pilot, built by Autocar. The White 24AX 12-cylinder engine provided power. The rear suspension was the same as that of the T16, with driven rear axles. The front clip of the T17 tapered toward the front, necessitating the use of fenders, which were simple, flat plates. A machine gun pulpit was over the right side of the cab. (Patton Museum, both)

Above: *Bows for a tarpaulin are installed on the Half-Track Truck T17 at Aberdeen on 25 June 1943. A dealer's license plate, X3779, state illegible, is strapped to footman loops on the rear of the body. Also on the rear were an entry door, channel-type bumperettes, tow pintle, electrical socket and cover, and two taillight assemblies. (Patton Museum)*

Below: *Pilot number one of Half-Track Truck T17 is undergoing analysis by the Armored Force Board, Test Division, at Fort Knox, Kentucky. Unlike Autocar-built pilot number two, the White-built first-pilot T17 lacked the machine-gun pulpit over the cab. Note the step made of bent steel strapping below the side of the cab. (Patton Museum)*

Above: *The White second pilot Half-Track Truck T17 had much more substantial front fenders than the flat plates used on the Autocar T17, with bent edges for extra strength and angled fronts that met the front bumper. The registration number is faintly visible on the hood: 40149398. The bottom-hinged armored windshield is lowered in this photo. The tail pipe is to the* front of the bogie frame. (Kevin Emdee collection) **Below:** *As seen in this close-up view of the left rear suspension of the White T17, the two sets of bogie wheels closest to the bogie frame were smaller than the other bogie wheels. Those two sets were 10-inch wheels. By contrast, all of the bogie wheels on the Half-Track Truck T16 were of the same size. (Patton Museum)*

Above: *The first pilot Half-Track Truck T17 is seen from above during tests at Fort Knox. The seating arrangement was two in the cab, two rear-facing seats to the rear of the cab, and five inward facing seats on each side of the cargo compartment, for a total of 14. To the rear of the seats in the cargo compartment were spacious stowage bins. Fuel tanks were to the sides of the* two rear-facing seats. (Kevin Emdee collection) **Below:** *The first-pilot White Half-Track Truck T17 and a Half-Track Personnel Carrier M3 were posed side by side for comparative purposes during the T17's tests at Fort Knox. The T17 had a stated personnel capacity of 14, only one more than the M3 could carry, but the personnel in the T17 were less crowded. (Patton Museum)*

Above: *The tarpaulin and canvas tops are installed on the second-pilot Autocar Half-Track Truck T17. As was standard practice for U.S. Army half-tracks, these covers were secured with straps to footman loops attached to the vehicle. Whereas the White T17's armored windshield was bottom-hinged and lay atop the hood when lowered, the Autocar T17 had a top-hinged armored windshield held up by four supports when raised.*

Below: *The second-pilot Autocar Half-Track Truck T17 displays its tarpaulin in a view from the left front. Another difference between the Autocar and the White pilot T17s was that the Autocar version had doors on the side of the cargo compartment, similar to those on the Half-Track Car M2. Note the triangular supports under the front ends of the fenders. (TACOM LCMC History Office, both)*

Above: *It was likely during mobility tests that the White Half-Track Truck T17 became mired in a mud flat. On the front of the hood is a feature not present in earlier photos of this T17: a pair of sprung hold-down clamps for the hood panels. Faintly visible on the side of the hood is the registration number, 40149398. "ECONOMY SIZE" had been painted on the lower part of the driver's door. A radio-antenna post is to the rear of the cab. (Chris Benedict collection)* **Below:** *In 1941 Mack Manufacturing Corporation manufactured two pilot half-track trucks designated* the T19. The vehicle had a snubbed front end, as the Continental R6572 six-cylinder, water-cooled, gasoline engine was mounted in the rear. The vehicle had an unpowered front axle and ran on 11 9/16 inch-wide tank tracks instead of the band-type tracks used on the other half-track trucks. The equalized volute spring suspension employed light-tank sprockets, idler wheels, and bogie wheels. Shown here is the second pilot T19 on 18 December 1942 while undergoing tests by the Ordnance Operation, General Motors Proving Ground, under Project 115. (Patton Museum)

Above: *A large ventilation grille/door for the engine compartment dominated the rear end of the Mack Half-Track Truck T19, as seen in a photo of the second pilot. A door with two bottom hinges and latches at the top corners was on each side of the body to the rear of the cab; these provided access to ammunition compartments. To the rear of that door are several markings: in chalk at the top is "Received 12/10/42" over "#8146." The number 8146 is stenciled below the chalk markings, below which, faintly visible, is the registration number, 4015648.*

(Patton Museum) **Below:** *The second pilot T19, registration number 4015648, is seen during testing at Aberdeen Proving Ground on 25 June 1943. A tarpaulin is installed, and the zippered side slit is open. On the right side of the front of the cab is the access door for the winch with two leaf hinges at the top and a grab handle at the bottom. Below the door is an opening in the bumper for the winch cable. Oversized brush guards protected the non-detachable service headlights. (NARA)*

Above: *In another 25 June 1943 photo of T19 4015648, a muffler and shield not present in the 18 December 1942 photos of this vehicle have been added to the top rear of the engine compartment. To the lower left of the grille/door is a coupling for compressed air for a trailer, protruding through a rectangular opening in the body. (NARA)* **Below:** *The first T19 pilot,*

registration number 4015647, is viewed from the rear during analysis by the Armored Force Board, Test Operation, at Fort Knox, Kentucky. The tarpaulin extended to the front of the engine compartment, and its rear curtain had a zippered, curved panel, shown partially open. Below each tail light was a flexible mud flap. (Kevin Emdee collection)

Above: *The Half-Track Truck T19 had a single-piece armored windshield to protect the two glass windshields behind it. Four swiveling arms supported the armored windshield when raised. Five bows supported the tarpaulin: four tall ones and a short one above the rear of the cab. (Kevin Emdee collection)*

Right: *Faintly visible to the front of the grille on the rear end of the second pilot Half-Track Truck T19, as photographed at Aberdeen Proving Ground on 10 May 1944, is a five-bladed radiator fan as well as pulleys and belts. Atop the vehicle are the muffler and guard that were added as a modification. The tracks reportedly were the same type used on the M3 Stuart light tank. (Patton Museum)*

Above: Three half-track trucks are viewed from above, presumably at Fort Knox, providing a rare glimpse into their interiors. In the foreground is the first pilot Half-Track Truck T19. Note the arrangement of the crew seats, the ammunition compartments, engine compartment, and the air cleaner in the recess on the left side of the engine compartment. In the middle is the first pilot Half-Track Truck T16, registration number 4015650. A fuel tank is visible in the right front of the cargo compartment, and seat backs and stowage bins and compartments are visible. The farthest vehicle is the second pilot Half-Track Truck T17, with the antenna support, right fuel tank, and stowage bins in view. (Chris Benedict collection) **Below:** At Aberdeen Proving Ground on 25 June 1943, three half-track trucks are lined up for a comparative photo. From left to right, they are the second pilot T19, the first pilot T17, and second pilot T16. The tarpaulin on the T19 has both of its side panels open. A .50-caliber machine gun is on the pedestal mount in the cargo compartment of the T16. (NARA)

Top: *From left to right are Half-Track Trucks T17, T16, and T19 during tests by the Armored Forces Board at Fort Knox, Kentucky. The photo was taken to demonstrate the vehicles' comparative heights.* **Above:** *The same three vehicles are viewed from the rear to compare their respective heights. From left to right they are the T17, T16, and T19. After Army testing proved these three pilot half-track trucks unsatisfactory, the program was discontinued in favor of full-tracked high-speed tractors. (Chris Benedict collection, both)*

Addendum A:
Half-Track Miscellany

Revisiting Topics from Book One

As is so often the case, no matter how thorough the research or meticulous the planning, seemingly as soon a book is bound and ready to ship new material is discovered.

Such is the case with the photographs presented here and in the next addendum. While the subject of the photos should have dictated that this information have been included in Part 1 of this series, fate demanded otherwise. Unfortunately, the material was not discovered until well after those books had been printed and delivered. Rather than allowing this material to languish in dusty filing cabinets for several more years, until such time that volume may be revised and reprinted, we opted instead to include them in this volume.

The use of deliberately outfitted half-tracks as field ambulances has previously been only spottily documented. While in Part 1 we were able to document the conversion kits, and provide a few photographs, the new photos in this addendum reveal previously unknown details concerning the ambulance conversions to the M3. While today the ambulance conversion is largely forgotten, it was sufficient consequence that pages of the Office of Chief or Ordnance – Detroit *Statistical Work Sheets, July 1944*, related to these vehicles are titled "Half Track, M3 Series as Personnel Carrier & Ambulance."

Interestingly, this document also lists the distribution of the vehicles as of that date, which includes 70 M3-series vehicles allocated to the U.S. Navy and

Marine Corps (along with 14 M2-series, and 175 M3A1 Scout Cars). No M15, M15A1 or M16 or mortar carriers are shown in this document as being allocated to the Navy or Marines.

Also further illuminated in this addendum is the development of passenger grab handles in the M2 and M3, as would be dictated by Modification Work Order (MWO) G102-22. Also presented is the installation of the obscure headlamp stowage box, associated with the 21 June 1943 MWO G102-34. This MWO directed the installation of removable armored vehicle style headlights rather than the original truck-style headlight on those half-track vehicles with mounted weapons if sufficient caliber to cause concussive damage to headlight bulbs.

These are followed by images of the bonding strap installation, required for radio suppression, and an important detail for enthusiasts. This addendum closes with an assortment of rare images of International Harvester half-tracks in U.S. service. The International Harvester M5 and M9 series vehicles were designed and produced specifically for Defense Aid (Lend-Lease), and only rarely saw use by U.S. forces. Some of these were taken during evaluation by the Armored Force Board at Fort Knox, but even more significant are those taken during training by the 12 Armored Division in Texas.

The Armored Force Board at Fort Knox, Kentucky, experimented with converting Half-Track Personnel Carriers M3 to evacuating carriers for troops wounded in combat. Here, four litter patients are loaded in a half-track. Chains with rings on them and U-shaped holders secured the litters in place. (Jim Gilmore collection)

Four litter patients covered with blankets are loaded in an M3 four-litter evacuating carrier, with two attendants in front of them and three soldiers seated in the cab. Conditions were cramped for both the patients and the crewmen. (Jim Gilmore collection)

The same configuration of four litter patients and five crewmen in an M3 evacuating-carrier half-track is viewed from the front. A close examination of the photo shows that the U-shaped holders for the front inboard handles of the litters were on a bracket attached to the machine-gun pedestal. (Jim Gilmore collection)

In this configuration, two litter patients are on the right side of the M3 evacuating-carrier half-track and four ambulatory patients are seated on the left side, along with the five-man crew. Two litters are stored to the rear of the men on the left side of the vehicle. (Jim Gilmore collection)

Above: *An Armored Force Board photograph taken at Fort Knox shows the configuration of a four-litter evacuating carrier as seen through the open rear door. There was barely enough room for an attendant to move between the litter patients.*
Below:*In a view of the rear of the personnel compartment in an M3 half-track four-litter evacuating carrier, the chains and* rings that held the rear inboard handles of the litters are fastened to the rear door in approximately the position they would be in when litters were loaded. Also visible are U-shaped holders for the outboard rear handles of the top litters. The outboard sides of the bottom litters rested on the crew seats. (Jim Gilmore collection, both)

Above: *Medical supplies for use in an M3 half-track evacuating carrier are displayed. Items include sterile gauze, safety pins, adhesive tape, emergency medical tags, absorbent cotton, and carrying bags.* **Below:** *The five-man crew of a 4-Litter Carrier Evacuating Half-Track M3 at Fort Knox, Kentucky pose next to their vehicle with their medical gear and personal equipment. (Jim Gilmore collection, both)*

The ride in a U.S. half-track of World War II could be a rough proposition during cross-country operations. Hence, the Armored Force Board at Fort Knox experimented with installing handrails in a Half-Track Personnel Carrier M3. Those rails are visible to the fronts of the bench seats in the personnel compartment. (Wayne Hlavin collection)

The M3 modified with handrails at Fort Knox is shown with two crewmen sitting on the bench seats and grasping the rails. (Wayne Hlavin collection)

Above: *A handrail, more like a grab handle, was affixed to the right side of the middle seat in the cab of the Half-Track Personnel Carrier M3 at Fort Knox, as viewed through the windshield.* **Below:** *The Armored Force Board also ran tests with handrails in a Half-Track Car M2 at Fort Knox. Two soldiers are seated in this vehicle, holding onto the rails, as viewed from the cab. (Wayne Hlavin collection, both)*

Above: A 7 January 1942 taken for the Armored Force Board at Fort Knox documents the position of a handrail installed for the use of the assistant driver, across the well in the floor to the front of the right seat of an unidentified type of half-track. In the foreground are an axe and the battery box. **Below:** The front end of a Half-Track Car M2 is shown in a photo taken by the White Motor Company Advertising Department on 10 May 1943. It provides useful details for the detachable headlight assemblies, brush guards, tow hooks, and hood hold-down clamps. (Wayne Hlavin collection, both)

Above: *In the fall of 1942, experiments were conducted with a metal box to store four detachable, or pedestal-type, headlight assemblies in and on an M3 personnel-carrier half-track. Several positions for mounting the box were tested. Here, in a 2 October 1942 photo, the box is attached to the interior of the* vehicle to the rear of the right door. **Below:** *Here, the headlight storage box is tried on the center of the rear of the M2. A close-up view also is available of the folding storage racks and the machine-gun tripods secured to the rear of the vehicle. (Wayne Hlavin collection, both)*

Left: *The headlight-storage box is shown with the lid open and one detachable headlight assembly positioned inside. The interior of the box was divided into four compartments and was padded with a very coarse felt-type material. (Wayne Hlavin collection)*

Below: *Four detachable headlights are in the box. One of the service headlight assemblies was inserted upside-down to provide clearance for the hood of the single blackout headlight to the upper right. (Wayne Hlavin collection)*

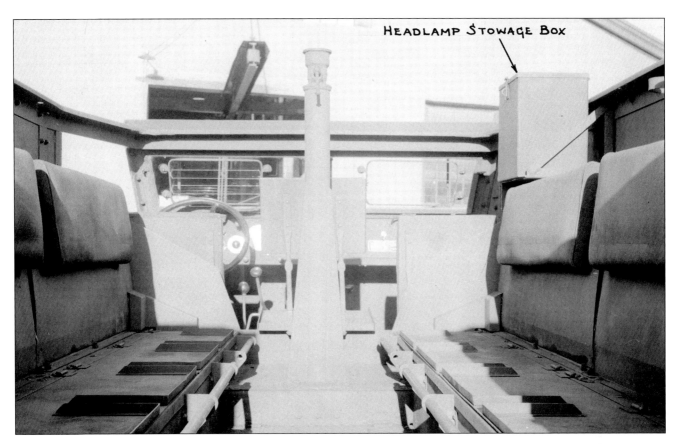

HEADLAMP STOWAGE BOX

Above: *This final view of the headlight storage box, dated 18 November 1942, shows it on the interior of an M3 half-track personnel carrier, as seen from the rear of the crew compartment. It was positioned on a rack supported by a diagonal brace. Note the detachable defrosters mounted on the windshield.* **Below:** *A Half-Track Personnel Carrier M5 is shown during analysis by the Armored Force Board Test Operation at Fort Knox, Kentucky. The nickname "MURIEL" is painted on the right door. The full canvas top is installed. The M5 was International Harvester's version of a half-track personnel carrier and was distinguished by simplified front fenders and rounded rear corners of the body. (Kevin Emdee collection, both)*

The underside of a well-used International Half-Track Personnel Carrier M5 is viewed from a service pit in a 1943 photograph. At the top is the anti-ditching roller. Flexible boots are on the joints between the front axle and the steering knuckles. Visible farther back are elements of the drive train, the rear axles and suspension, and the exhaust. (Wayne Hlavin collection)

Above: *The original caption of this photo identifies the vehicle as a Half-Track Car M9, but the presence of the machine-gun pulpit suggests it was remanufactured to M9A1 standards. The registration number, 40104253, is faintly visible on the hood. The nickname "JEAN" is painted on the right door, and on the side of the body is stenciled "ARMORED FORCE BOARD / TEST OPERATION / 609." (Kevin Emdee collection)*

Below: *The same Half-Track Car M9 upgraded to M9A1 standards seen in the preceding photograph is viewed from the left rear at Fort Knox, Kentucky, during testing by the Armored Force Board. The rounded rear corners of the body are clearly visible from this angle. Because of those rounded corners, a horizontal brace was necessary at the rear of the mine racks to secure them to the body. (Kevin Emdee collection)*

Above: *The rounded rear corners of the body and the lack of a ring mount help to identify this vehicle as an International Harvester Half-Track Personnel Carrier M5. The scene was at Camp Bowie, Texas. An M4A3 Medium Tank is on the second flatcar. (12th Armored Division Memorial Museum)*

Below: *An unidentified soldier poses with an IH Half-Track Personnel Carrier M5 with markings for the 17th Armored Infantry Regiment, 12th Armored Division, at Camp Barkeley, Texas. To the right is an IH Half-Track Car M9A1, registration number 4069212. (12th Armored Division Memorial Museum)*

Above: *Members of B Company, 56th Armored Infantry Battalion, pause for a break during a field exercise at Camp Barkeley, Texas. The straight fenders without skirts and the lack of ring mounts help identify these vehicles as IH Half-Track Personnel Carriers M5. The vehicles carried X-shaped tactical signs with small letters and numbers on their sides.* **Below:**

Half-Track Personnel Carrier M5 registration number 4029531 was assigned to the 12th Armored Division. A tarpaulin is rigged over just the center and rear bows. On the side of the body of the vehicle, between the front of the soldier's head and the rear of the driver's door, are two of the footman loops for strapping down the tarpaulin. (12th Armored Division Memorial Museum, both)

Above: Members of the 12th Armored Division take a break with their half-tracks during a training exercise. The closest vehicle is either an M5A1 or M9A1. The middle vehicle is identifiable as an M5 by the sharp angle of the inner front corner of the left front fender, IH-style left headlight and brush guard, and the lack of a ring mount. **Below:** During a training exercise,

Sergeant Stan Folkman pauses for a smoke break at the rear of a Half-Track Personnel Carriers M5. On the bumperettes are markings for the 15th vehicle in the column of march of Company C, 56th Infantry Regiment, 12th Armored Division. (12th Armored Division Memorial Museum, both)

Two G.I.s enjoy a bottle of wine on the hood of a half-track exhibiting the style of fenders and headlight/brush-guard combination characteristic of International Harvester vehicles. The presence of a ring mount marks this as a Half-Track Personnel Carrier M5A1 or Half-Track Car M9A1. A water-cooled Browning .30-caliber machine gun is on the ring mount. (12th Armored Division Memorial Museum)

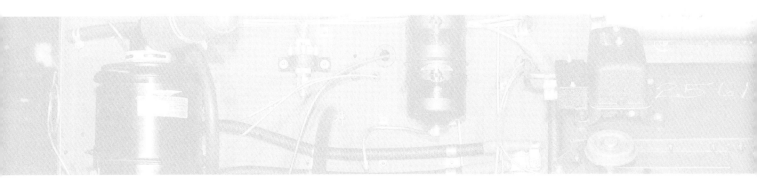

Addendum B: M3 Scout Car

Additional Information on Diesel Scout Cars

As discussed in Part I of these series, the SNL G-102 series of half-tracks are directly descended from the White scout cars. While there is a strong resemblance between the vehicles, in fact few components will interchange between the two types. This is somewhat surprising given that White built chassis for both types, essentially at the same time, and Diebold made the armored bodies for both the White-built half-tracks and the White scout car—and that both were Standardized vehicles.

However, in addition to the Standardized M3A1, which was powered by the Hercules JXD engine, a number of test vehicles were procured with Diesel power plants. The Buda 6DT-317 and a Diesel version of the JXD, the Hercules DJXD, were used in this pilot program. While the tests were largely successful, U.S. Army policy at that time dictated that gasoline engines be used in combat vehicles. Thus, shortly after the conclusion of the field-testing, the decision was reached that the Diesel scout cars would be salvaged for parts common to their gasoline-powered brethren.

After the publication of Part I, a cache of previously unknown photographs, taken by White in Cleveland and by the Army at Aberdeen, was located and are presented in this appendix.

Also appearing in this appendix are a number of newly discovered factory photos of early-production standard M3A1 Scout Cars. Because these photos divulge previously unseen details, they too have been included.

Also discovered since the publication of Part I was a 20 December 1943 letter from Brigadier General John K. Christmas, Assistant Chief, Tank-Automotive Center to Brigadier General W. P. Boatwright, Commanding General, Office of Chief of Ordnance – Detroit.

This letter reads: "In view of the fact that the Scout Car M3A1 is being withdrawn from United States troops (the Light Armored Car M8 and Utility Car M20 being used instead), and there will shortly be non or practically none of these vehicles in service in the continental United States, I, therefore, recommend that Stock Control be directed to put on a special drive to collect these parts, (both parts common and parts peculiar) from all installations in the United States, including posts, camps, stations and maintenance companies in the field, and segregate them promptly in one depot. This is particularly important because scout cars are being furnished to both the Russians and the British and as you know, they are literally screaming for spare parts. To the first of November 18,448 of these vehicles have been manufactured of which about 6,300 were in service in the United States and about 4,000 were in storage in the United States. Unless strong immediate action is taken on this, there valuable parts will be lost to us and we will be under continuing pressure from the Allied Nations to get parts from industrial sources. These parts are also badly needed for our remanufacturing program which at present consists of 2,000 scout cars to be remanufactured."

A Scout Car M3A1 chassis is viewed from the rear. In the foreground is the rear bumper and tow pintle, followed further forward by the rear axle and wheels, rear propeller shaft, fuel tanks, battery (right), transmission, steering wheel and dashboard, front fenders, engine, and radiator. Also in view are the exhaust, muffler, and tailpipe. (Wayne Hlavin collection)

Above: *A factory-fresh, early-production Scout Car M3A1 is displayed with the canvas top installed and a crossed sabers U.S. Cavalry emblem affixed to the door. Characteristics of the early M3A1 included civilian-style headlights and spotlight, and eight-hole front wheels.* **Below:** *The transfer case of the M3A1 was mounted under the special cross member of the chassis at the center of the photo, with a small propeller shaft connected to the transfer and the transmission (right). At the upper center is the left fuel tank. To the right are the dashboard, the instrument panel, the steering wheel, the transmission shift lever, transfer-case shift lever, and brake lever. (Wayne Hlavin collection, both)*

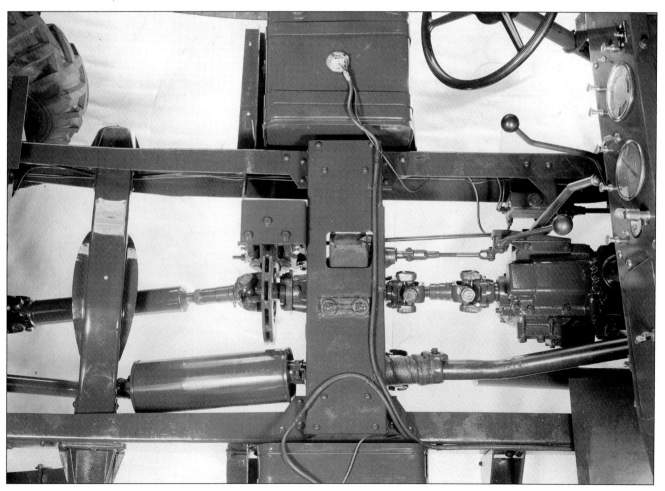

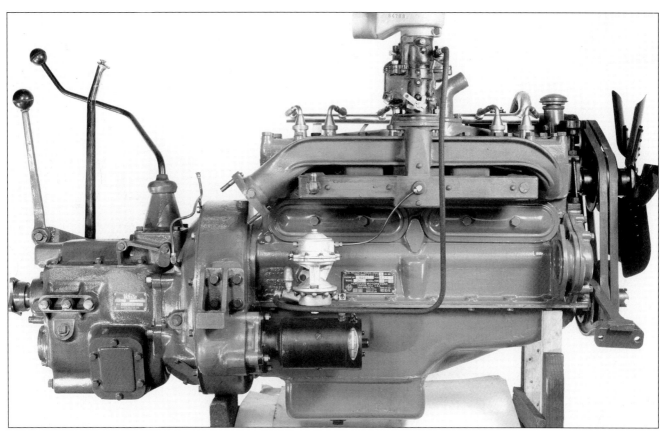

Above: *A Hercules JXD engine for a Scout Car M3A1 is seen from the right side. This example was serial number 926401. To the rear of the engine is the transmission, manufactured by White, serial number 80092. Even the carburetor air intake (top) had a White logo and the part number in raised letters, 34733.* **Below:** *The dash assembly of a Scout Car M3A1 is viewed from the front. To the left is the oil bath air cleaner. On the opposite side of the firewall are the ignition coil and shield assembly (the horizontal, light-colored object) and the voltage regulator. In the middle are the vacuum check valve and fuel filter. At the lower right is the horn. (Wayne Hlavin collection, both)*

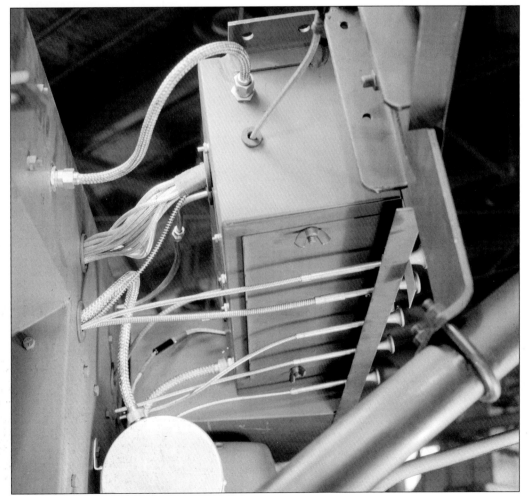

Above: The dash assembly of an M3A1 is seen from the rear. At the center of the dashboard is the instrument panel, with the door of the glove box open to the right. The louvered object below the right side of the dashboard is the crew heater, and the shiny cylinder to the left of it is the radio filter. (Wayne Hlavin collection)

Below: This view of the dash of an M3A1 was taken from the left side of the lower part of the steering column looking upward into the area behind the dashboard. The instruments were enclosed in the metal box. Also visible are the electrical harnesses and lines for the instruments and controls and, toward the lower left, the side of the radio filter. (Wayne Hlavin collection)

Above: *The dash of an M3A1 is installed on the chassis, complete with steering wheel and steering column. On this example, the heater is a Tropic-Aire model. To the left of the heater is the radio filter, which in this instance has been painted a glossy color. Also in view are the left fuel tank (lower right); the top of the transmission; the transmission and transfer-case shift levers; and the hand-brake lever. (Wayne Hlavin collection)*

Below: *The Hercules JXD gasoline engine installed in an M3A1 is observed from the right side. The oil-bath air cleaner to the left has the decal of the United Air Cleaner Company, Chicago, Illinois. Below the air cleaner is the horn. On the side of the engine below the carburetor is the exhaust and intake manifold, with an I-beam appearance. Below it is the engine intake manifold, of boxy shape. (Wayne Hlavin collection)*

The interior arrangements of an early-production Scout Car M3A1 are shown in this overhead photo. Later on in production of the M3A1, the solid supports for the machine-gun skate rail on the sides and at the rear of the crew compartment were replaced by U-shaped support brackets of various size: smaller ones along the sides and rear and a large one at each rear corner. (Wayne Hlavin collection)

Above: *The Hercules JXD engine installation is seen from the left side. Toward the front of the engine is the generator assembly. The thick, braided cable over the generator is routed to the distributor below the generator. To the rear of the distributor is the water-pump assembly. The light-colored, disc-shaped object above the large flex hose was the vacuum-booster air cleaner. (Wayne Hlavin collection)* **Below:** *As seen from the cab of a*

Scout Car M3A1 at Aberdeen Proving Ground on 25 November 1940, 12,000 rounds of .30-caliber machine-gun ammunition are loaded into the boxes in the crew compartment. According to the original caption of the photo, there also were 550 rounds of .45-caliber submachine gun ammunition in the boxes. (Jim Gilmore collection)

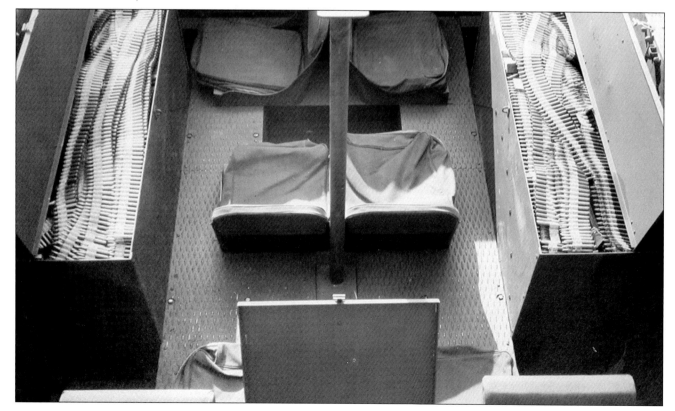

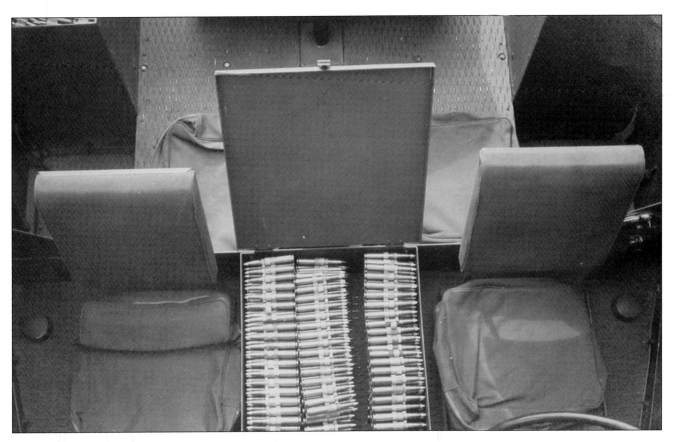

Above: *In the same M3AI depicted in the preceding photo, 750 rounds of .50-caliber machine-gun ammunition are stored in the box between the two front seats. The bottom seat cushions were actually shells with zippers so that folded blankets could be stuffed inside for cushioning. The blankets evidently were not inserted in these cushions. (Jim Gilmore collection)*

Below: *In this view through the right door of a Scout Car M3AI, the folded blankets are inserted in the bottom seat cushions. The horizontal fixture visible on the right door is a three-position door stop, a feature of early-production M3AIs, which allowed for setting the maximum outer swing of the door at three different angles. (Wayne Hlavin collection)*

Above: *This is a view through the right door of an M3A1 look-ing toward the left rear of the vehicle. In the foreground is part of the bulkhead between the cab and the crew compartment, on the other side of which are the forward back-to-back personnel seats. To the upper left is what seems to be a rack or metal cabinet installed in the center of the personnel compartment.*

Below: *M3A1 6010608 is viewed from another angle while undergoing flexibility and stress tests. Mismatched wheels are on this vehicle: the front one is a solid-disc combat wheel, and the rear one is the intermediate-pattern six-hole wheel. (Wayne Hlavin collection, both)*

Above: *Scout Car M3A1 registration number 6010608 is being subjected to stress and flexibility tests by driving the left front and right rear tires over ramps. This was to replicate driving over extremely rough terrain and was to ensure that the suspension, chassis frame, and bodywork were not stressed to the breaking point under such conditions. (Wayne Hlavin collection)*

Left: *This photograph and the following one are related to the photograph at the top of page 69 in the author's book,* The Military Machine, Volume One: Half-Tracks. *They depict elements of a deep-water wading kit for a Scout Car M3A1 in the form of a substitute exhaust pipe that extended up through the cab to the rear of the right A-column of the windshield. This photo shows the remodeled portion of the exhaust in the engine compartment. (Wayne Hlavin collection)*

Left: *The special exhaust for a deep-water wading kit for an M3A1 is viewed at the point where it enters the right front of the cab. The idea of the revamped exhaust was to expel exhaust fumes above the water level as the vehicle made its fording. (Wayne Hlavin collection)*

Below: *This image augments the photographs on page 66 in The Military Machine, Volume One: Half-Tracks. The Hercules DJXD engine was used in the Scout Car M3A2, later redesignated the M3A1E5, but here it is shown installed in an M3A1, serial number 2451, at Aberdeen Proving Ground, on 3 August 1942. The DJXD was a six-cylinder, compression-ignition-type Diesel engine with overhead valves and four-stroke operation. It had a displacement of 339 cubic inches and 103 brake horsepower at 2,600 rpm. (Jim Gilmore collection)*

Above: *The same Hercules DJXD engine is seen from farther back, showing more of the Scout Car M3A1 it was installed in. Crossing diagonally over the top of the engine is the air hose from the air cleaner in the right rear of the engine compartment to the air-intake venturi on the left side of the engine block. The venerator is to the front of the air-intake venturi. (Jim Gilmore*

collection) **Below:** *The following section of photographs can be considered a supplement to the photos of the Scout Car M3A1 on pages 67 and 68 in* The Military Machine, Volume One: Half-Tracks. *Seen here is a Scout Car M3A1E1 chassis, which was distinguished by the Buda-Lanova 6DT-317 Diesel engine. (Wayne Hlavin collection)*

Above: *This photo of a Buda-Lanova 6DT-317 Diesel engine installation in a scout car served as the basis for an illustration of the right side of the engine in the Scout Car M3A1 tech manual, TM9-705. Features include the air cleaner, oil filter, and horn (left); the pressure fuel pump (light-colored mechanism at the center); and the fuel filter, the governor, and the oil filler and breather (right). (Wayne Hlavin collection)*

Right: *The right side of the Buda-Lanova 6DT-317 engine installation is seen from a slightly different angle. On the near side of the valve cover is the exhaust manifold, below which is the intake manifold. The oil filter to the right was the Deluxe Clear-Oil Filter manufactured by the De Luxe Products Corporation, La Porte, Indiana. Both the pressure fuel pump and the fuel filter next to it were American Bosch products. (Wayne Hlavin collection)*

A scout car chassis with a Buda-Lanova 6DT-317 Diesel engine is viewed from above. The vacuum pump and its air and oil reservoir, the single cylinder head cover, the exhaust and intake manifolds, and the air-intake hose are clearly visible. (Wayne Hlavin collection)

Above: *In a view of the left side of a Buda-Lanova 6DT-317 Diesel engine installation in a scout car, to the left is the belt-driven vacuum pump above the generator. The vertical cylinder at the center is the vacuum pump air and oil reservoir. To the right, mounted on the dash, are the voltage regulator and the vacuum booster air cleaner. (Wayne Hlavin collection)*

Right: *This photo and the subsequent ones provide clearer views of a Buda-Lanova 6DT-317 Diesel engine. Below the oil filter toward the rear of the engine block is the starting motor. This engine had six cylinders and a displacement of 317 cubic inches. (Wayne Hlavin collection)*

430

Above: *The right side of the 6DT-317 engine is seen from another angle. Dominating the center of the engine block is the American Bosch pressure fuel pump, with six fuel lines attached to couplings on the top of the unit. The right rear engine support bracket is fastened with four hex screws to the side of the bell housing. (Wayne Hlavin collection)*

Below: *The Buda-Lanova 6DT-317 engine is viewed from the rear. To the left of the cylinder head and its cover are the vacuum pump and the generator, and to the right are the exhaust manifold, the air intake elbow, and the oil filter. To the bottom are the bell housing, flywheel, and the rear engine supports. (Wayne Hlavin collection)*

Above: *The generator was specified as a heavy-duty, four-brush, shunt-wound unit, with shielded terminals to diminish radio interference. It had a maximum cold output of 55 amperes, as controlled by the regulator. Affixed to the center of the cylinder head cover is a small placard giving the firing order (1-5-3-6-2-4) and instructions on setting the tappets. (Wayne Hlavin collection)*

Below: *The boxy oil pan is visible at the bottom of the Buda-Lanova 6DT-317 as seen from the left front. Running along the side of the engine is the cylinder water inlet manifold, to the immediate rear of which is the Buda-Lanova manufacturer's plate. (Wayne Hlavin collection)*

Appendix

Motor Carriage Contract and Registration numbers

Qty	Type	Contract	PO	Registration number	Ord serial #	Make
279	M4	W-741-ORD-6285	T-540	see note	see note	White
47	M4	W-303-ORD-1179	T-3186	4083236 thru 4083282	280-326	White [1]
46	M4	W-303-ORD-1179	T-3186	4083190 thru 4083235	327-372	White
200	M4	W-303-ORD-1294	T-3374	4082990 thru 4083189	373-572	White
372	M4A1	W-303-ORD-2078	T-4310	4060918 thru 4061289	573-944	White [1]
228	M4A1	W-303-ORD-4011	T-4782	40105141 thru 40105368	1747-1974	White [1]
110	M21	W-303-ORD-4011	T-10838	40172914 thru 40173025	3-112	White [1]
36	T12	W-670-ORD-1796	T-1915	409528 thru 409613	1-86	Autocar
50	T12	W-670-ORD-1796	T-2052	409528 thru 409613	1-86	Autocar
1,350	M3-75	W-670-ORD-1765	T-3042	4017060 thru 4018409	87-1436	Autocar
30	M3-75	W-670-ORD-2597	T-4073	4053350 thru 4053379	1437-1466	Autocar
736	M3-75	W-670-ORD-2597	T-4163	4053724 thru 4054349	1467-2092	Autocar
962	T48	W-271-ORD-1023	T-3513	4020934 thru 4021614	Unknown	Diamond T
312	T30	W-303-ORD-945	T-3212	409582 thru 409893	4004-4303	White
188	T30	W-303-ORD-1611	T-3967	4042505 thru 4042584	315-394 [2]	White
324	T19	W-324-ORD-6289	T-3191	403377 thru 402698	2-323	Diamond T
1,103	M13	W-303-ORD-1860	T-4031	4048234 thru 4048768	1-535 [3]	White
1,605	M14	W-271-ORD-2502	T-4402	4083887 thru 4085491	1-1605	International Harvester
110	T10E1	W-33-019-ORD-578	T-10718 [1]	40172310 thru 40172419	8011-8120	White [4]
1,897	M16	W-303-ORD-1860	T-4031	4048769 thru 4051233	1-2465	White
568	M16	W-303-ORD-1860	T-4031	Included within above [5]	—	White
802	M16	W-303-ORD-4672	T-6648	4061290 thru 4062091	2466-3267	White [1]
178	M16	W-303-ORD-5334	T-7844	40122706 thru 40122883	3268-3445	White [1]
60	M16	W-33-019-ORD-2982	T-17610	Unknown	8121-8180	White/Diebold [6]
1,000	M17	W-271-ORD-2502	T-11082	40175244 thru 40176243	1-1000	International Harvester
80	T28E1	W-670-ORD-2627	T-4081	4053380 thru 4053459	1-80	Autocar
600	M15	W-670-ORD-3216	T-4356	4083287 thru 4083886	81-680	Autocar
1	M15A1	Unknown	T-9427	40148306	681	Autocar
1,652	M15A1	W-670-ORD-4816	T-8050	40149399 thru 40151050	682-2333	Autocar

1. With winch.
2. Balance of 108 vehicles on this order were converted to M3A1 Personnel Carriers per production order T-19179.
3. 568 vehicles converted to M16, thus the shortfall in serial and registration numbers.
4. T10E1 converted to M16 per contract 33-019-2097 PO T-17610.
5. Built as M13 by White and converted to M16 prior to shipment.
6. Built as M13 by White, converted to M16 by Diebold Safe and Lock Company.

Note concerning contract W-741-ORD-6285, production order T-540 M4 production: Registration numbers 4015366-4015497; serial numbers 1-132. Registration number 4015499; serial number 133. Registration numbers 4015506-4015507; serial numbers 134-135. Registration number 4015509; serial number 136.

The following tables supersede the similar tables appearing on page 432 of Part 1

M3E2 tabulated data

Qty.	Year	Contract	PO Number	Model/Make	Registration number range	Ord. serial number range
1	1943	W-271-ORD-1452	T-3762	M3E2	403307	3429
1	1943	W-271-ORD-1452	T-3762	M3E2	409422	3844
7,519	1943	W-271-ORD-1426	T-3781	M5	4029247 – 4036765	11259 through 18777*
65	1943	W-271-ORD-2769	T4936	M5A1	40101631 – 40101695	8070 through 8134**

* The winch/roller split of 4,286 w/winch, 3,233 w/roller is per IH data, Ordnance has 4,287 w/winch; 3,232 w/roller.

** This order, issued on 7 November 1942, originally called for 1,000 M5 equipped as ambulances, and on 16 December 1942 was modified to specify standard M5 vehicles. On 29 December 1943 the order quantity was reduced to 65 vehicles. The winch/roller split per IH data is 37 w/winch, 28 w/roller; Ordnance has 36 w/winch/29 roller.

M2E5 tabulated data

Qty.	Year	Contract	PO Number	Model/Make	Registration number range	Ord. serial number range
2	1943	W-271-ORD-1452	T-3762	M2E5/IH	4015156 – 4015157	4958-4959
3,433	1942	W-271-ORD-2643	T-4660	M9A1/IH	4067586 – 4071018	3- 3435*

* An additional 1,102 vehicles on this contract were cancelled.

This US Marine Corps M16A1 was photographed at 29 Palms, California, during operation "FEX" in December 1952. The USMC markings are plainly visible on the rear stowage boxes as well as the engine compartment side panels. (NARA)

Bibliography

Monographs

Hunnicutt, R. P., *Half-track A History of American Semi-Tracked Vehicles*: Novato, CA: Presidio Press, 2001. ISBN: 0-89141-742-7

Stanton, Shelby L., *World War II Order of Battle*: New York, NY: Galahad Books, 1984. ISBN: 0-88365-775-9

Noville, G.O. & Associates, *Weapons Mounts for Secondary Armament*, Detroit, MI: G.O. Noville & Associates, 1957.

Zaloga, Steven J., U.S. Half-Tracks in Combat 1941-1945: Hong Kong, New Territories: Concord Publications Co., 1999. ISBN 962-361-654-6

Technical Manuals

ORD 9 SNL G-147; Half-track vehicles: Car, half-track, M9 (M2E5) (International Harvester Co.); carrier, personnel, half-track, M5 (M3E2) (International Harvester Co.); carriage, motor, multiple gun, M14 (International Harvester Co.); carriage, motor, multiple gun, M17. September 1, 1943

TM 9-707, Basic Half-Track Vehicles (IHC) (Personnel Carrier M5, Car M9A1, Multiple Gun Motor Carriage M14, and similar IHC Vehicles) May 21, 1943.

ORD 9 SNL G-102 List of All Parts for Half-Track Vehicles (White, Autocar and Diamond T), 1 December 1944

TM 9-1710C Ordnance Maintenance Chassis and Body for Half-Track Vehicles, September 11, 1942

TM 9-1711 Ordnance Maintenance White 160AX engine, Half-Track Vehicles, January 26, 1942.

TM 9-710 Basic Half-Track Vehicles (White, Autocar and Diamond T), 5 January 1942

TM 9-710 Basic Half-Track Vehicles (White, Autocar and Diamond T), 23 February 1944

TM 9-710 Basic Half-Track Vehicles (White, Autocar and Diamond T), 8 May 1953

ORD 7-8-9 SNL G-67 Ordnance Supply Catalog, Organizational Spare Parts and Equipment List Higher Echelon Spare Parts and Equipment List (Addendum) Spare Parts Catalog for Car, Scout, M3A1.

TM 9-705 Scout Car, M3A1 Operation and Maintenance, 19 February 1941

TM 9-705 Scout Car, M3A1 Operation and Maintenance, 26 October 1942

TM 9-1705 Scout Car, M3A1 Ordnance Maintenance Power Train (Axles, Propeller Shafts, Transfer Case, Transmission), 20 August 1942.

TM 9-1705C Scout Car, M3A1 Ordnance Maintenance Diesel Power Plant (Hercules DJXD Engine) 1 October 1942.

TM 9-1706 Scout Car, M3A1 Ordnance Maintenance Gasoline Power Plant (Hercules JXD Engine) 13 September 1942

TM 9-1709 Ordnance Maintenance Chassis and Body for Scout Cars M3A1, 22 September 1942

TM 9-1832A Hercules Engines, Series JX Models A, C, D, E-3, F, 17 May 1944

TM 9-2010 Multiple Caliber .50 Machine Gun Mounts M45, M45C, M45D, and M45F; Multiple Caliber .50 Machine Gun Trailer Mount M55 and Trailer Mount M20. 4 December 1953

Documents

Project Supporting Paper 48 and 49 Half Tracks, Tractors and Carriers

Summary Report of Tank-Automotive Material Acceptances, September 1 1945

Statistical Work Sheets, To 1 August 1945, Volumes 41 and 42, Office of Chief of Ordnance – Detroit.

Official Munitions Production of the United States, by Months, July 1, 1940 – August 31, 1945; Civilian Production Administration, 1 May 1947.

Lend-Lease Shipments World War II, Office, Chief of Finance, War Department, 31 December 1946.

Alphabetic Listing of Major War Supply Contracts, Cumulative, June 1940 through September 1945, Civilian Production Administration, Industrial Statistics Division. 1946

Half-track Military Vehicles, A History and Continuing Survey, Edmund Lieberman, 1 October 1944.

Ordnance Department Armored, Tank and Combat, Vehicles 1940, 1941, 1942, 1943, 1944; Records Section, Statistics and Analysis Branch, Stock Control Division, Office Chief of Ordnance – Detroit, 15 December 1944.

The Armored Force Board, Fort Knox, Kentucky, Project Number 136-8, Stowage and Equipment List for 4 Litter Carrier (Evacuating) Half-Track, M3, 26 May 1943.

Numerous Ordnance Committee Minutes and Aberdeen Proving Ground test reports.

Sitting in the turret of this Half-Track Multiple Gun Motor Carriage M16 and taking a break from scanning for enemy aircraft is Pfc. Fred Maloney of Company A, 19th Infantry Regiment, 24th U.S. Infantry Division. The photo was taken near Kumhwa, Korea, 30 September 1951, and shows the center panels of the bat-wing armor in the lowered position. (NARA)

On Both the Battle Front and the Business Front
DIEBOLD Equipment Meets America's Vital Needs!

We are keenly alive to the importance of peak capacity — but we also know how equally vital is the turning out of materials that will stand the gaff in the hour of supreme test.

Whether it be tanks, guns and airplanes armored against gruelling enemy shell fire, or bomb and flood-proof vaults, the Diebold ideals of honest value and willing service are back of every ounce of effort put forth.

Our entire resources are at Uncle Sam's command. They include the vast experience gained from over eighty years on the battle front of American Business. Today, the Diebold name on Cardineers, fire-resistive safes, vault doors or any one of a score of Diebold Business Tools is uni-

versally recognized as a symbol of efficiency and established quality.

We are proud to do our part in our nation's all-out war-time program. We know that business, more than ever before, needs Diebold products to carry on the part it must play in these exacting days.

Yes, we are working and producing as never before, but at the same time we are maintaining the Diebold high standards of quality, either on armor plate for government machines of war, or on business tools that speed up work, increase efficiency or protection, and help cut costs and increase profits. In the name of greater results — call or write Diebold.

DIEBOLD SAFE & LOCK CO.
Plants and General Offices: Canton, Ohio

For Faster Record-Processing in Both Office and Plant—

DIEBOLD *Cardineer* ROTARY FILE

Speeds posting and reference work. Saves valuable space. Portable. Thousands of records *on a wheel* instantly brought to operator's finger-tips. Readily adaptable to your present records—new records easily added. Your choice of manual or electric operation.

Write for folder.

The CARDINEER is helping hundreds of America's Business Leaders solve their increased war-record problems. Ask your local DIEBOLD MAN for a complete demonstration.

METHODS EQUIPMENT,
SAFES, MONEY CHESTS
ELECTRIC REKORDESK SAFES
BANK VAULTS, OFFICE ACCESSORIES

DIEBOLD

Offices in: New York, Chicago, Detroit,
Philadelphia, Washington, Cleveland,
Boston, St. Paul, Pittsburgh, St. Louis.
Dealers in other Principal Cities

DIEBOLD BUSINESS TOOLS PROTECT AND HOUSE AMERICA'S WEALTH AND RECORDS

Steve Andereggen, Jr. collection

DIAMOND T

Diamond T 105 millimeter "tank-destroyers" at the recapture of Sened oasis in Tunisia—a painting based on photographs officially released by the War Department

"The Guns that Go Anywhere" depend on Diamond T stamina!

CANNON-CARRIER, man-mover, trail-blazer, the amazing Half-Track is proving one of the most versatile weapons of this war. As shown in the picture, the mobile howitzer is a form of "tank-destroyer" that has brought consternation to the blitz-battlers of the Axis.

It is only one of Diamond T's contributions to the fighting power of our armed forces. As prime mover, wrecker, ponton and general cargo carrier, the 4-ton six-wheel-drive Diamond T is giving vital support in every major theater of war. And giant Diamond T "tank-recovery" units are shuttling shell-torn General Shermans to base repair echelons to be returned to battle with front-line performance renewed.

The "production-front" is delivering the goods. The E flag above our plant signifies excellence of product, and it applies to Diamond T production volume which is greater than the normal peace-time heavy-truck output of the entire industry.

A brilliant engineering staff and a redoubled production machine are devoted today to the winning of the war; when Victory has brought peace, they will celebrate with new and finer commercial trucks to carry even higher the splendid traditions of the famous Diamond T Super-Service line.

DIAMOND T MOTOR CAR COMPANY, CHICAGO

Established 1905

★ DIAMOND T MOTOR TRUCKS ★

OUT OF THIS WAR

International Red Diamond Engine. Heavy-duty power for heavy-duty work. Ample power and capacity—surprising economy. Proved in actual combat warfare, now available for civilian service.

The new Red Diamond Engine powers International Models K-8, KS-8, KR-11, and KS-11.

THIS BATTLEFIELD doesn't look much like a Pennsylvania truck terminal or a 4-lane highway. But out of mechanized war have come ideas that will benefit transportation, construction and agriculture the world over.

The rugged requirements of warfare on every battlefront have inspired the engineering genius of American industry. Out of this war came, for example, the *new International Red Diamond Engine.*

Tens of thousands of International Military Trucks and Half-Tracks—powered by this new International Red Diamond Engine—have set new transportation and combat records in wartime service.

Many of these mighty Red Diamond Engines have already gone into International Heavy-Duty Trucks for essential civilian use. The men who operate them will vouch for the stamina and economy of adequate power for any job.

The International Red Diamond Engine is *one* of the wartime developments International Harvester will pass on to the transportation industry.

When peace comes and new trucks roll out on America's highways, look to International for even greater economy, even greater dependability. And remember—for ten years before the war *more heavy-duty Internationals were sold than any other make.* Backed then, as now, by the *world's largest company-owned truck service organization.*

INTERNATIONAL HARVESTER COMPANY
180 North Michigan Avenue　　Chicago 1, Illinois

NEW TRUCKS: The government has authorized the manufacture of a limited quantity of light, medium and heavy-duty International Trucks for essential civilian hauling.

SERVICE: Many operators will have to wait for trucks. Maintenance of existing vehicles is just as important today as before V-E Day. Therefore—be sure your trucks get top maintenance and service at International Truck Dealers and Branches.

Buy More War Bonds and *Keep Them*

INTERNATIONAL

INTERNATIONAL *Trucks*

Now it's Tank *Destroyers*

STRIKING POWER...borne of more speed and mobility than any tank...makes these armored, cannon-bearing half-tracs—Tank *Destroyers*.

Newest of the Army's mechanized equipment, they are blood-brothers of peacetime motor trucks . . . a typical example of trucks in modern warfare.

White is devoting all its manufacturing resources to building war equipment. Second only to this, White accepts its obligation to help truck owners keep their trucks running. They are vital transportation links in a wartime economy. Every White Branch and Dealer is prepared to give every truck and bus owner a *definite* conservation plan.

THE WHITE MOTOR COMPANY, Cleveland

Builders of U. S. Army Tank Destroyers, Scout Cars, Half-Tracs, Prime Movers and Cargo Trucks, the complete line of Super Power Trucks and Tractors, City and Inter-City Coaches, Safety School Busses and the Famous *White Horse.*

White

FOR MORE THAN 40 YEARS THE GREATEST NAME IN TRUCKS

Steve Andereggen, Jr. collection

Protecting His Future

KNOWING how to run 'em and how to fix 'em "when the chips are down" is *important* to him. Keeping mechanized equipment in working order under tough combat conditions may mean life or death to the man over there.

VISUAL TRAINING AIDS help make sure that the men who use, maintain, and repair war products understand their operation and how to keep them running.

MEN CUSS what they don't understand and DISCUSS favorably the products they have learned to use right.

We are privileged to assist farsighted manufacturers who contribute to the training of men in the satisfactory use of their products. To other manufacturers we can give the benefit of much that has been learned in this important phase of the war effort.

The **JAM HANDY** *Organization*

Visualizations • Educational Sound Pictures • Slidefilms • Vocational Training

★NEW YORK	★WASHINGTON, D. C.	★DETROIT	★DAYTON	★CHICAGO	★LOS ANGELES
1775 Broadway	Transportation Building	2900 East Grand Boulevard	311 Talbott Building	230 N. Michigan Boulevard	7046 Hollywood Boulevard
COlumbus 5-7144	DIstrict 0611	MAdison 2450	ADams 6289	STAte 6758	HEmpstead 5809

Steve Andereggen, Jr. collection

Members of the 76th Antiaircraft Artillery Battalion, I Corps, are serving the gun of a Half-Track 40mm Gun Motor Carriage T19/M34 in defense of Taegu Air Force Base, Republic of Korea, on 13 January 1951. Seated is Pfc. Isaiah H. Brown, and standing behind him are loaders Cpl. Billie L. Christianson and Pfc. Raymond A. Miller. (NARA)